Black Torch

Story and Art by Tsuyoshi Takaki

Jiro Azuma is descended from a long line of ninja, and he also can talk to animals. One day, he rescues a very unique black cat named Rago, a supernatural being, and is dragged into a mystical war.

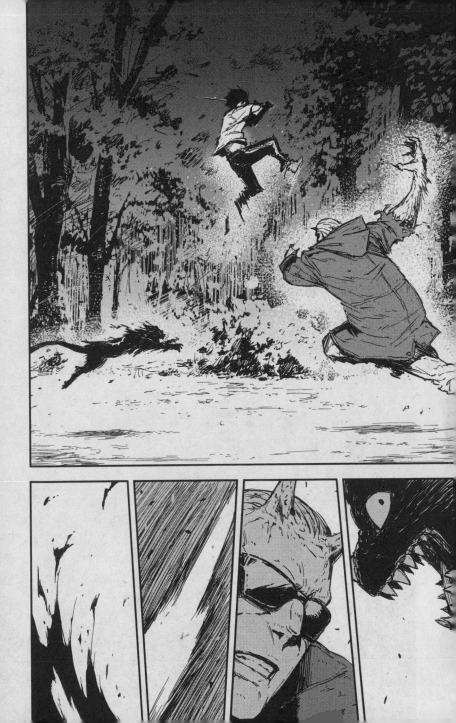

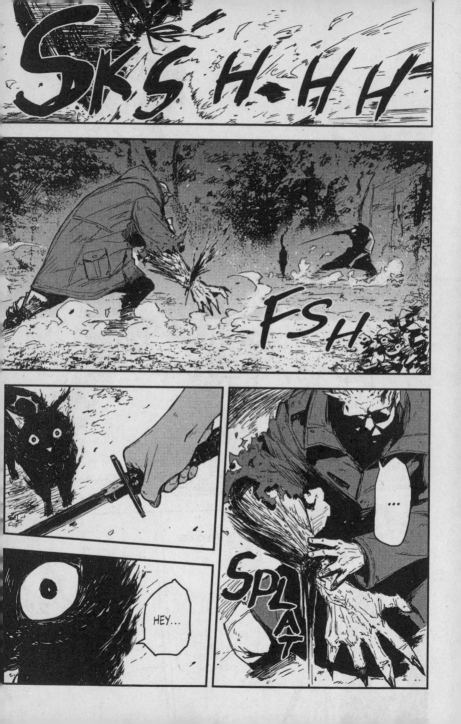

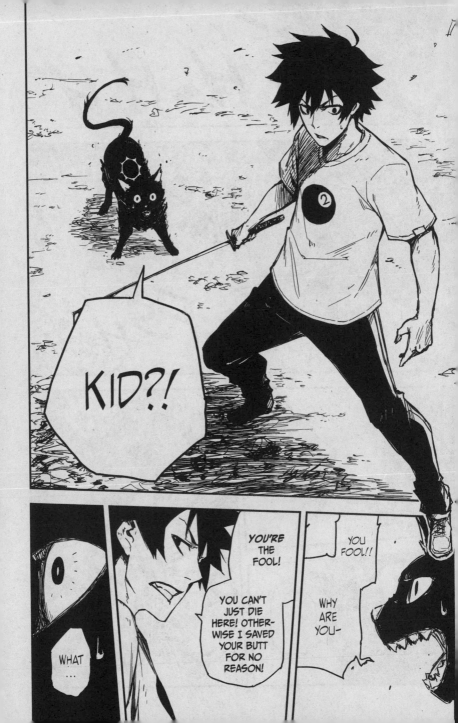

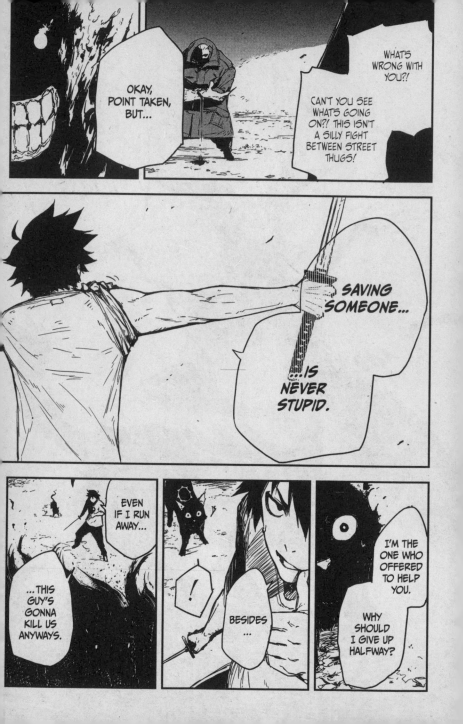

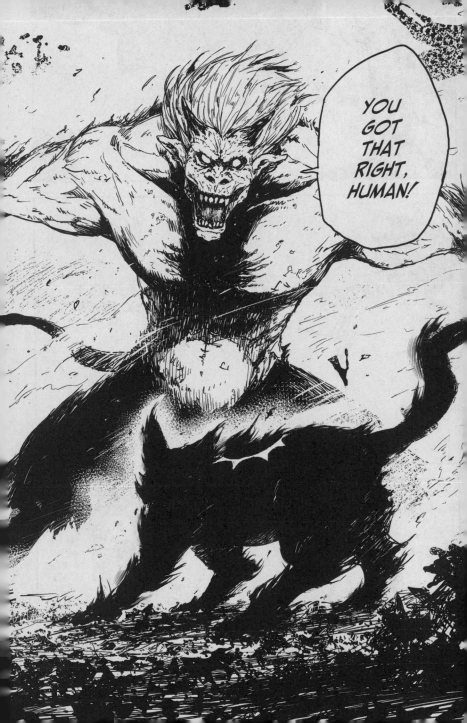

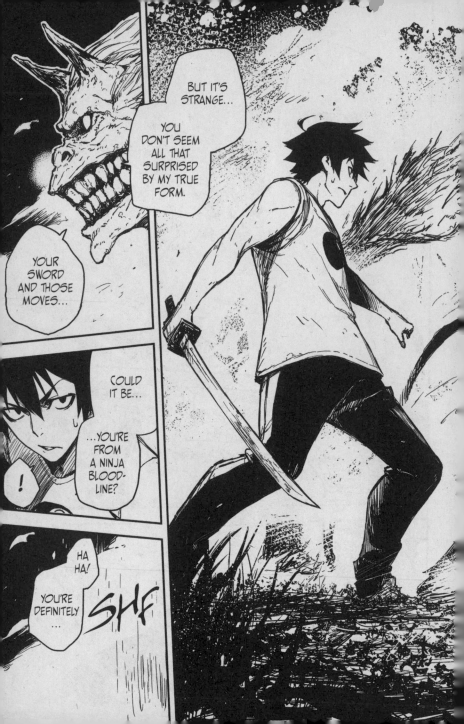

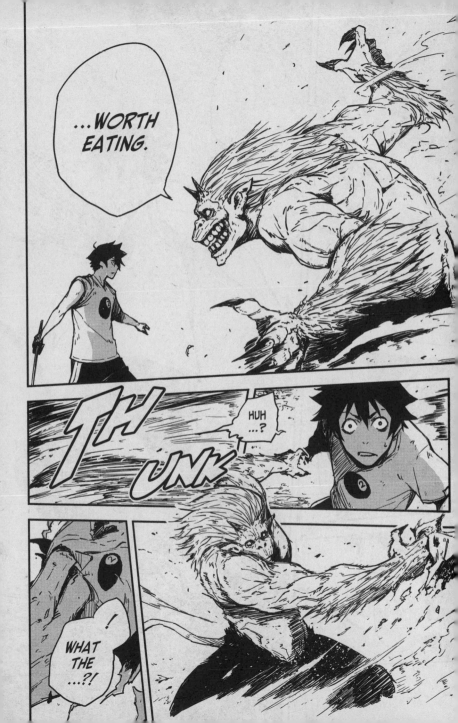

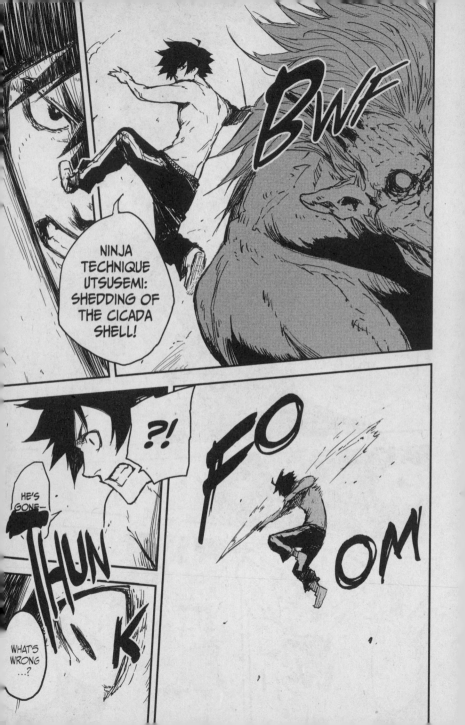

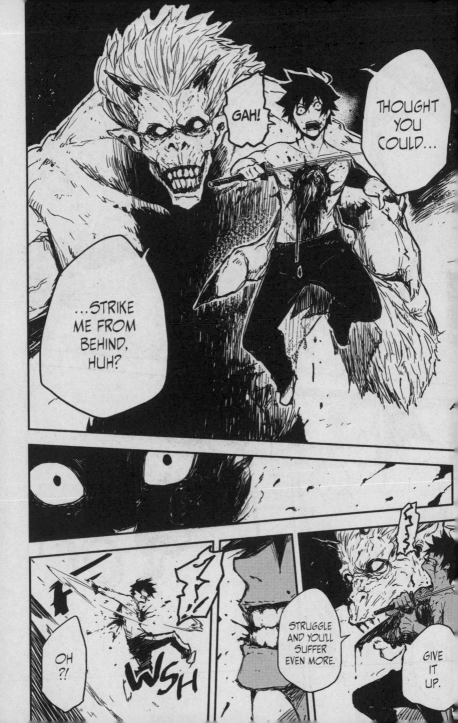

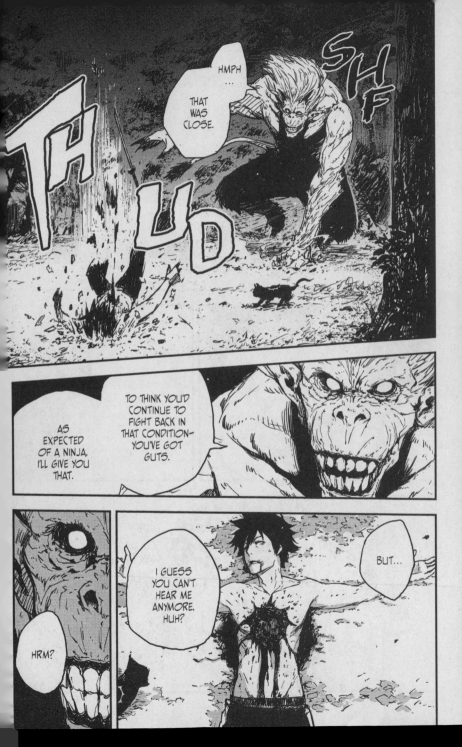

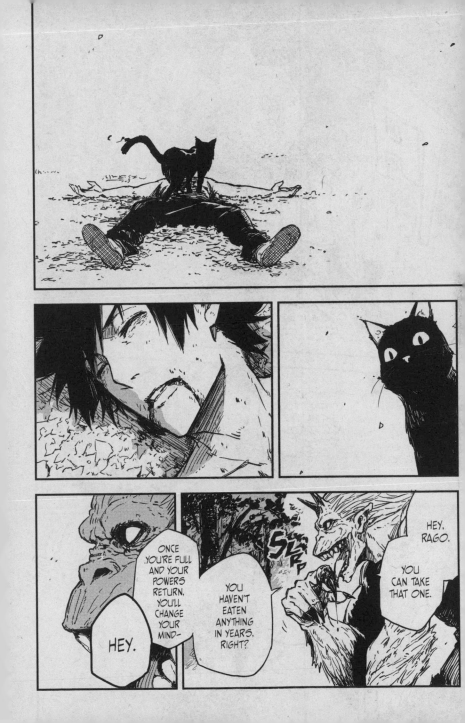

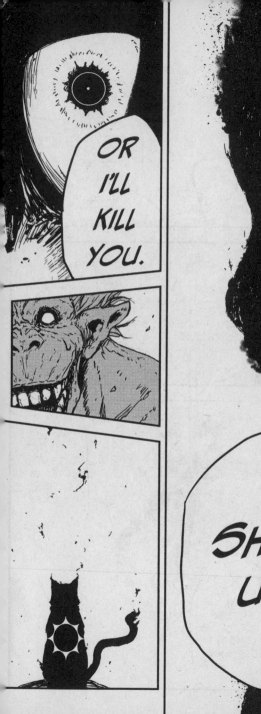
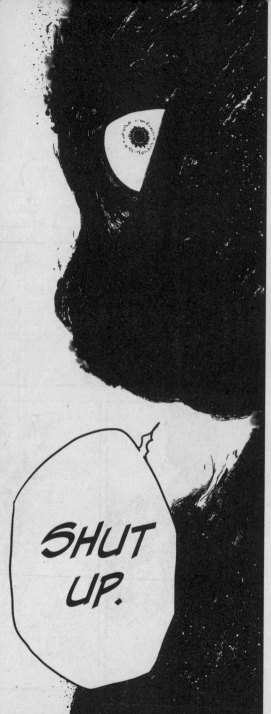

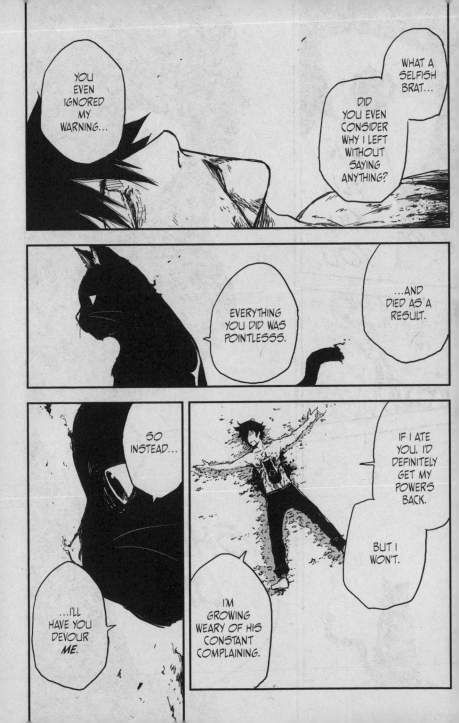

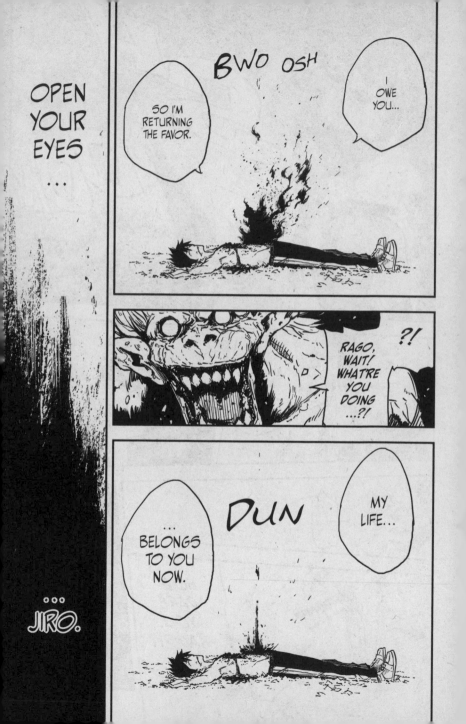

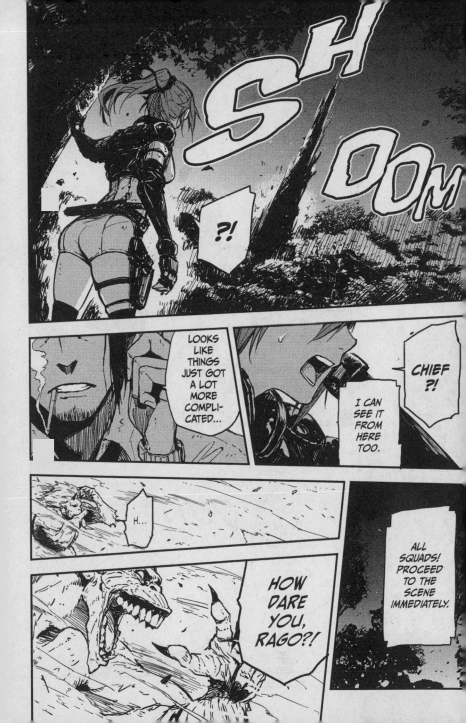

YOU...
DO YOU HAVE ANY IDEA WHAT YOU'VE DONE?!!
YOU GAVE YOUR POWER TO A HUMAN- TO A NINJA!!
YOU'VE ABAN-DONED YOUR OWN KIND...
DO YOU INTEND TO FIGHT FOR THE HUMANS?!
AH...
SHUT UP, DAMMIT...

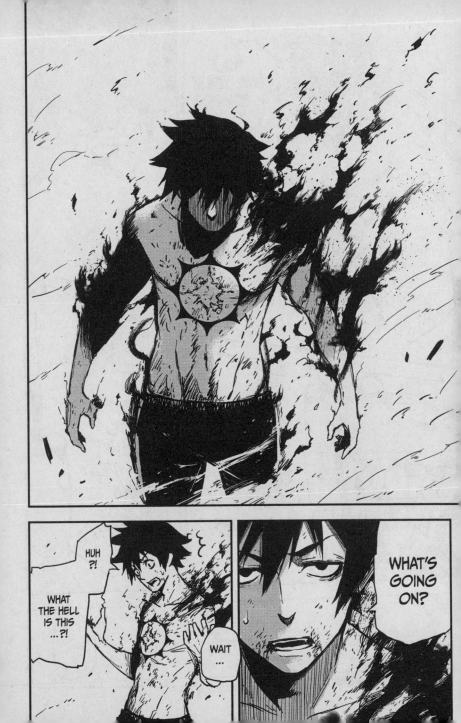

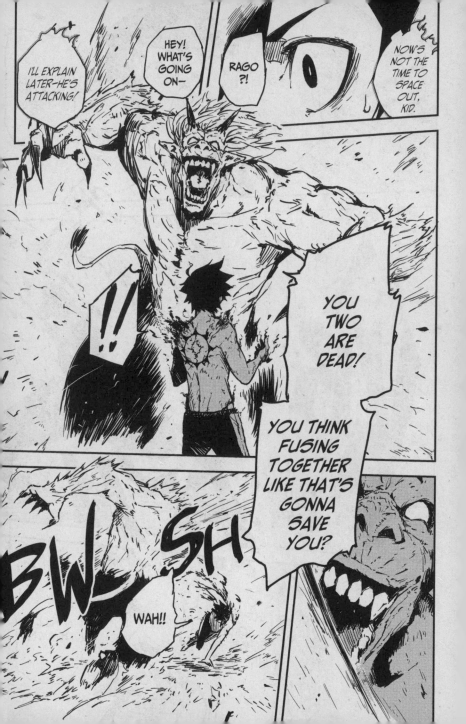

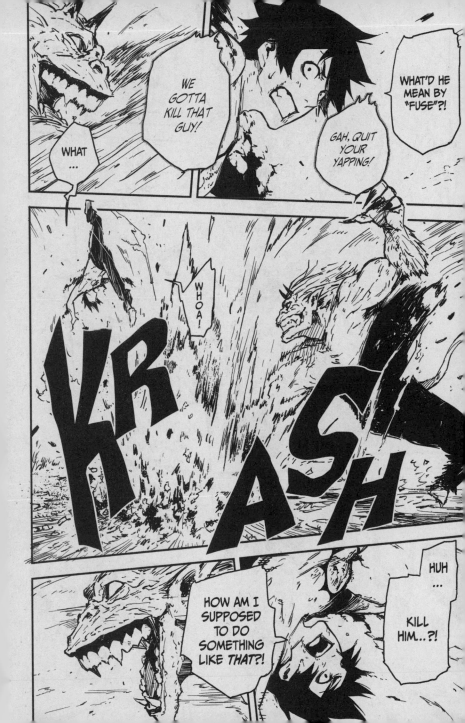

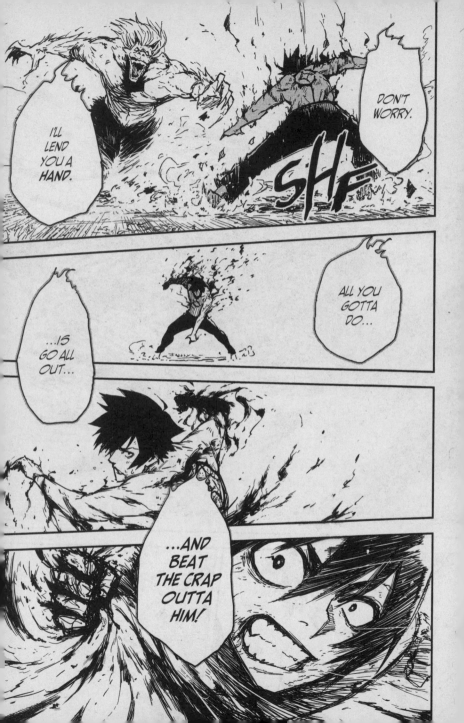

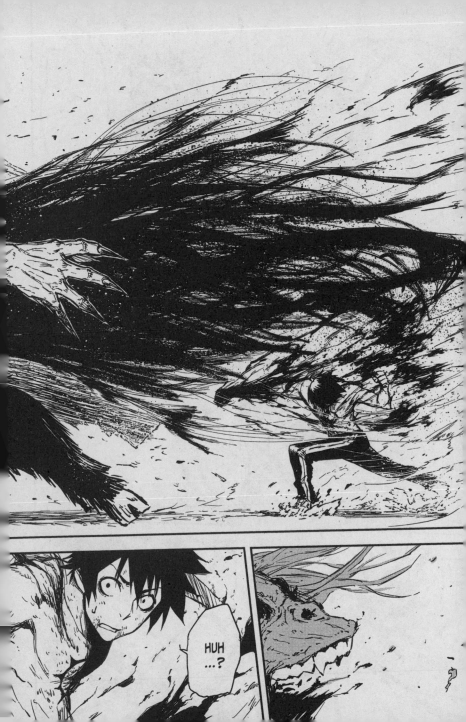

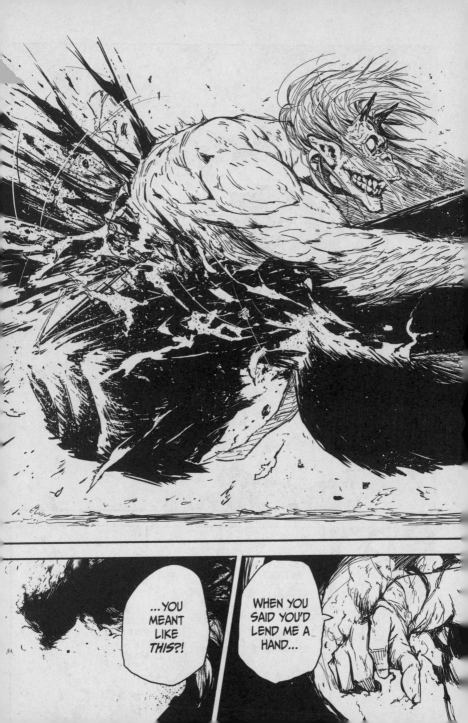

HUFF ...
HUFF ...
HUFF ...
FSHHHH
HUFF ... WHAT IN THE...
WHAT'S GOING ON?
ONE MOMENT, I WAS STABBED THROUGH THE CHEST.
AND NOW THIS BLACK SMOKE STUFF'S COMING OUT OF MY BODY...
HEY, YOU BETTER EXPLAIN EVERY-THING...
HUH? RAGO...?

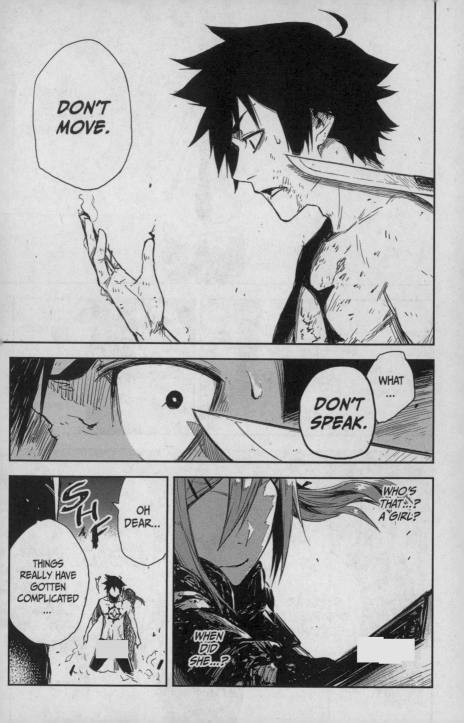

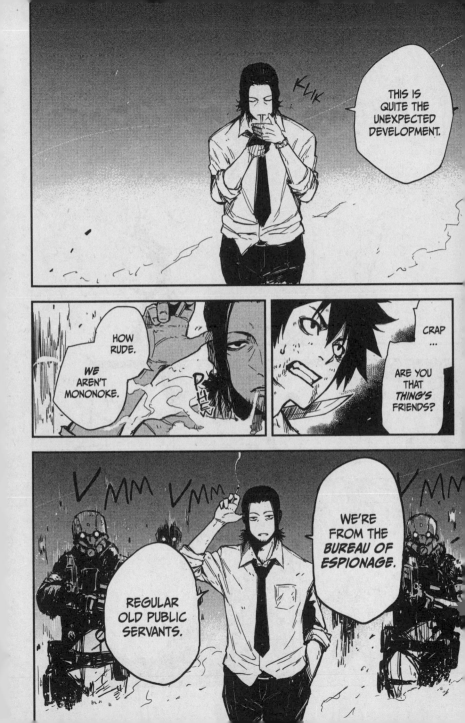

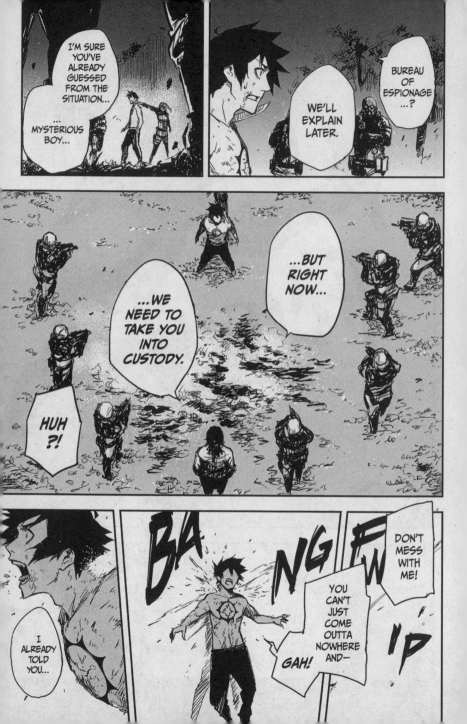

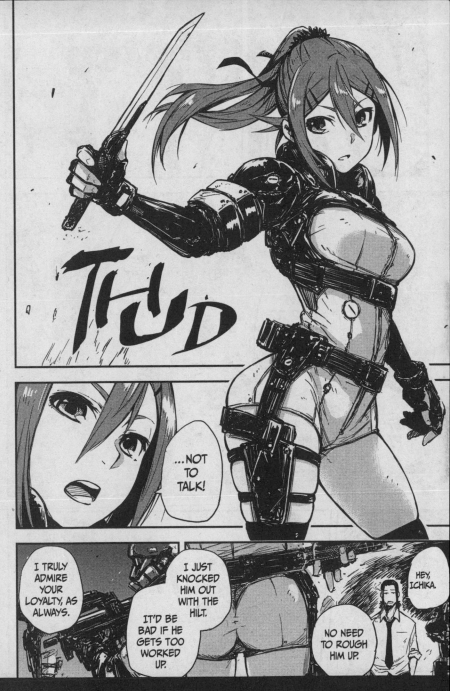

Kenka Bancho Otome: Love's Battle Royale

Created by Chie Shimada
Original concept by Spike Chunsoft
Video game developed by Red Entertainment

Hinako thought she didn't have any family, but on the day she starts high school, her twin brother Hikaru suddenly appears and tricks her into taking his place. But the new school Hinako attends in his stead is beyond unusual. Now she must fight her way to the top of Shishiku Academy, an all-boys school of delinquents!

HELLO!

Thanks so much for reading *Kenka Bancho Otome*.

YO!

Pleased to meet you. I'm Chie Shimada.

Never in my wildest dreams did I think a fighting game would become an otome manga!!

...but some of the scenes can only be found here in the manga.

This manga has been adapted from the game...

Merchandise

Don't forget to play the game too!

There are lots of related CDs and merchandise.

CD

Game

VITA

Kenka Bancho Otome

I'd never leave the nurse's office!

TOO SCARY!

Let's say I, Shimada, were to enter Shishiku Academy...

I CAN'T HANDLE DELINQUENTS!

Conclusion: Hinako is amazing!

At first I was surprised to see a school story without classroom scenes or teachers.

At school...

Find us on social media:

See you later!

Please check out volume 2 as well! Thank you for your support.

SUZUKAZE ORPHANAGE

HAVE A GOOD DAY, HINAKO!

YOU TOO!

ACK! IT'S HINAKO.

I'M HINAKO NAKAYAMA.

LET'S GET OUT OF HERE!

TMP TMP TMP

TODAY IS MY FIRST DAY AT KOTOBUKI GIRLS' HIGH SCHOOL.

I'VE BEEN LIVING AT SUZUKAZE ORPHANAGE FOR 15 YEARS.

I DIDN'T HAVE ANY FRIENDS ALL THROUGH MIDDLE SCHOOL.

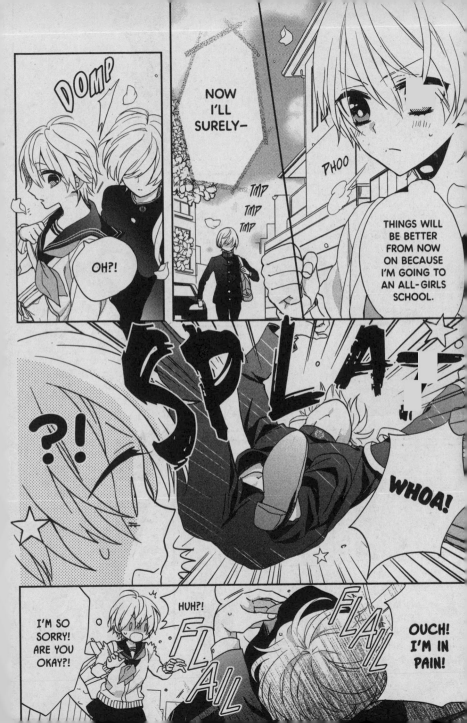

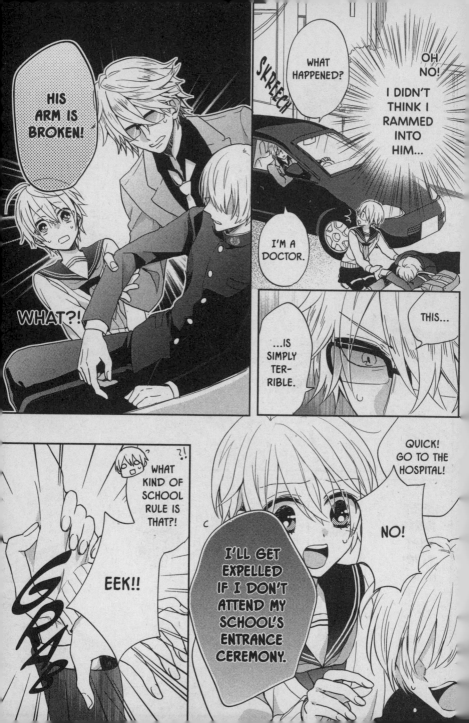

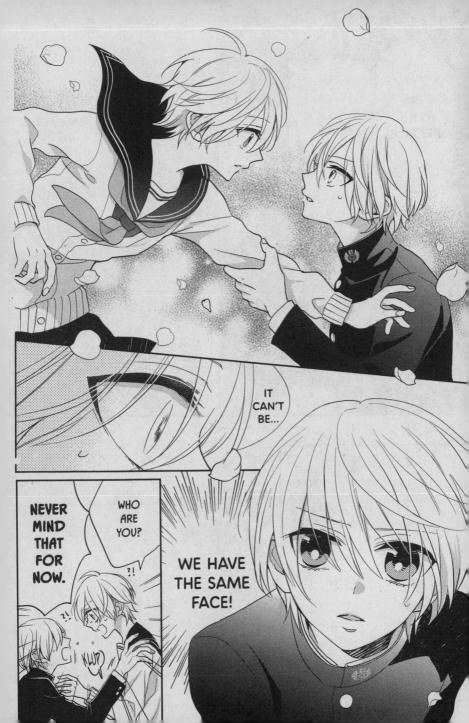

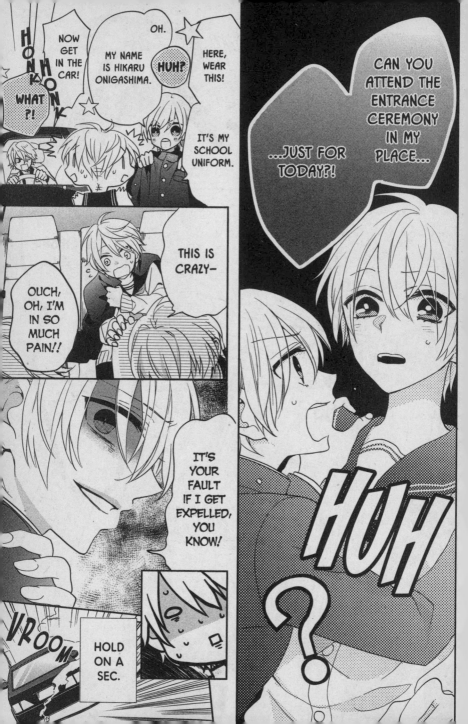

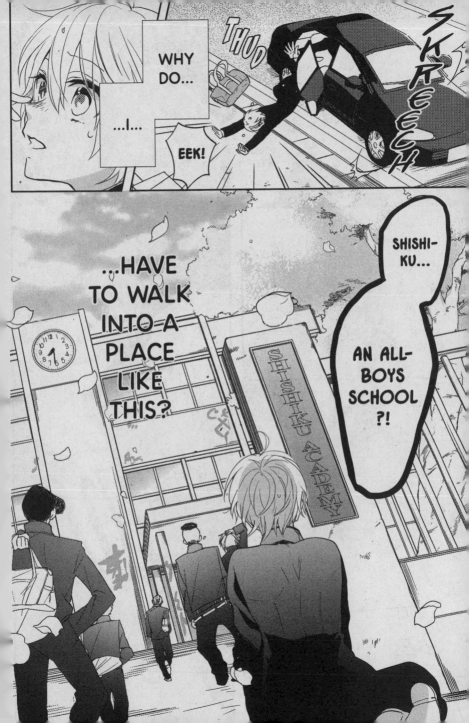

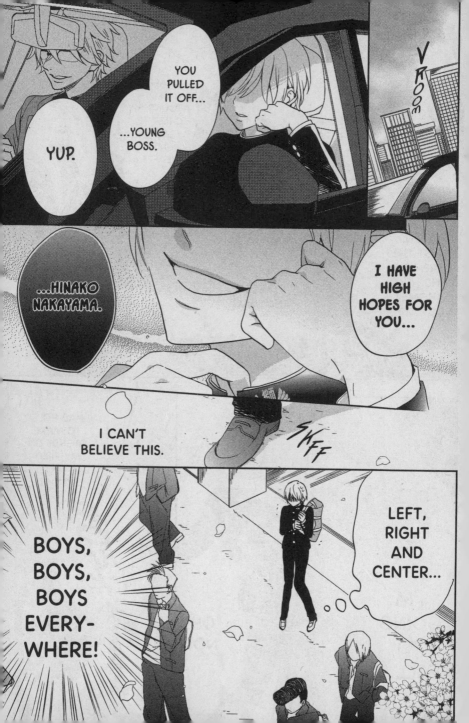

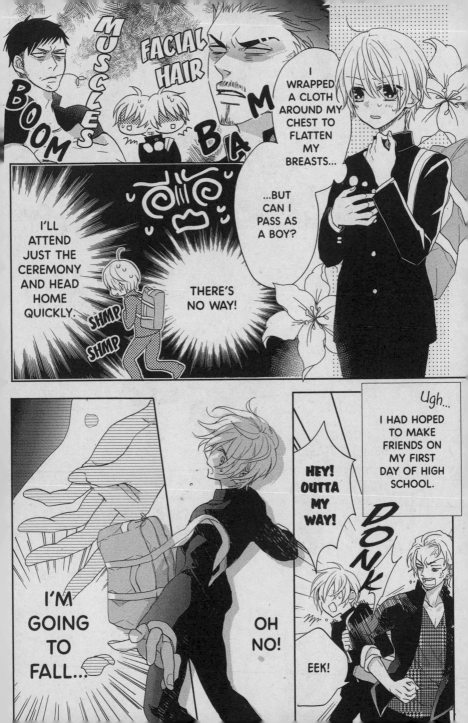

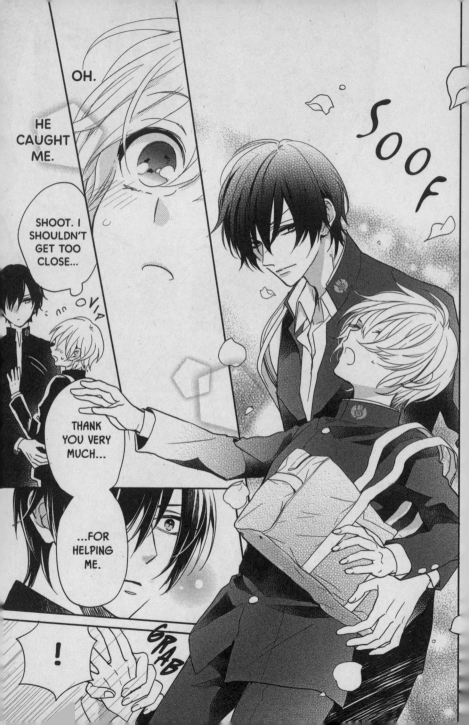

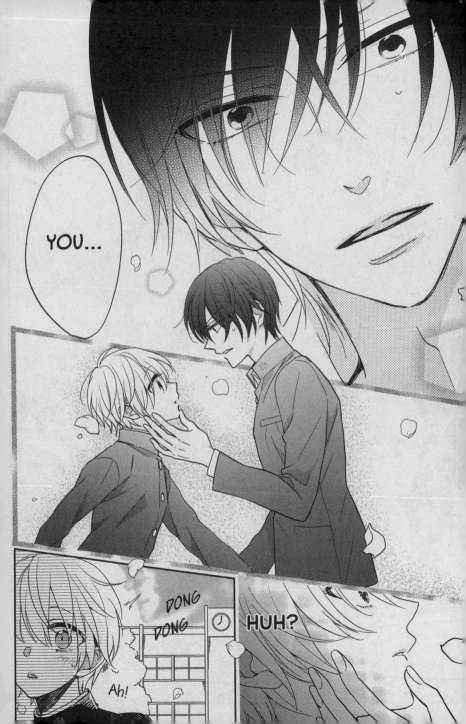

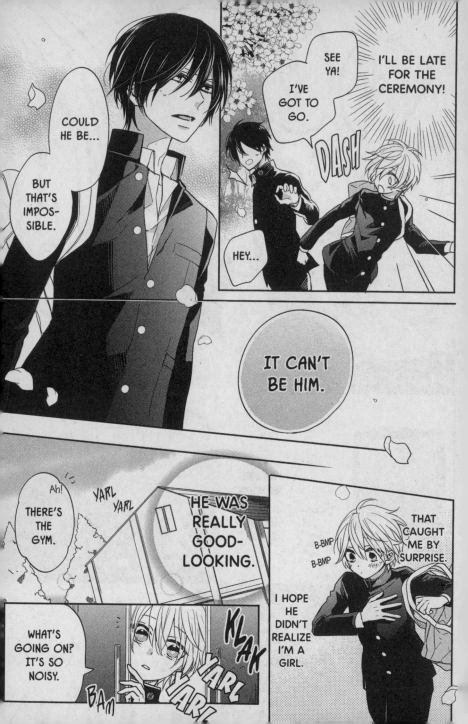

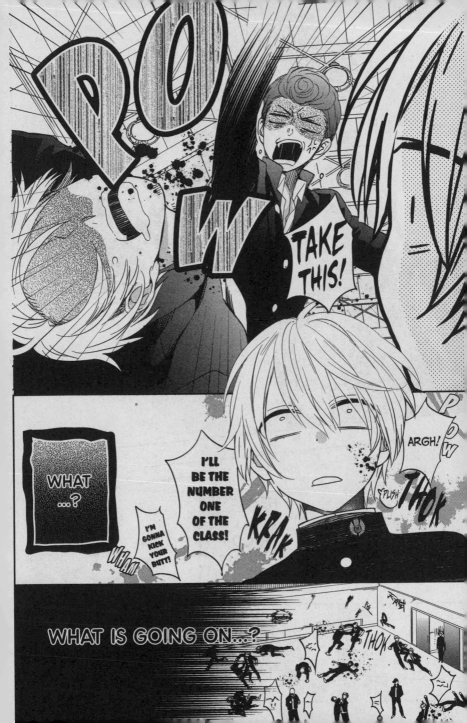

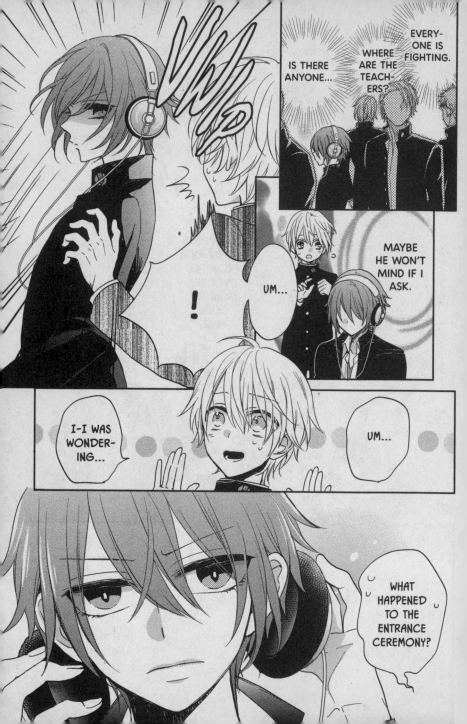

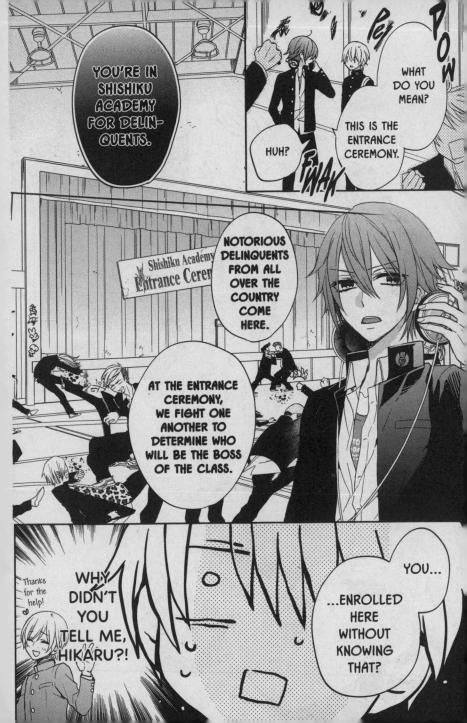

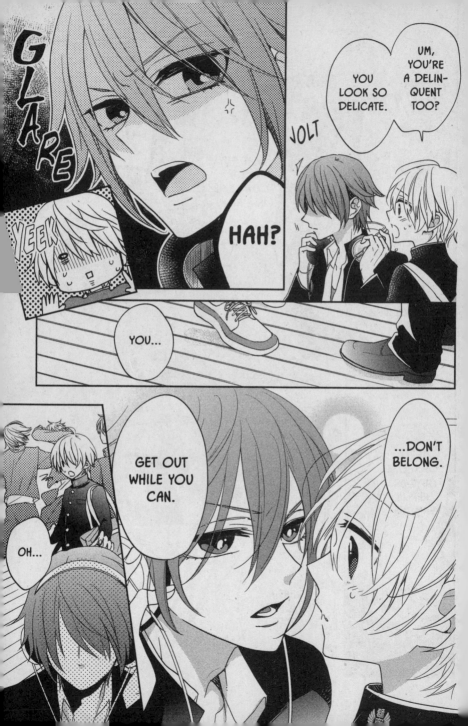

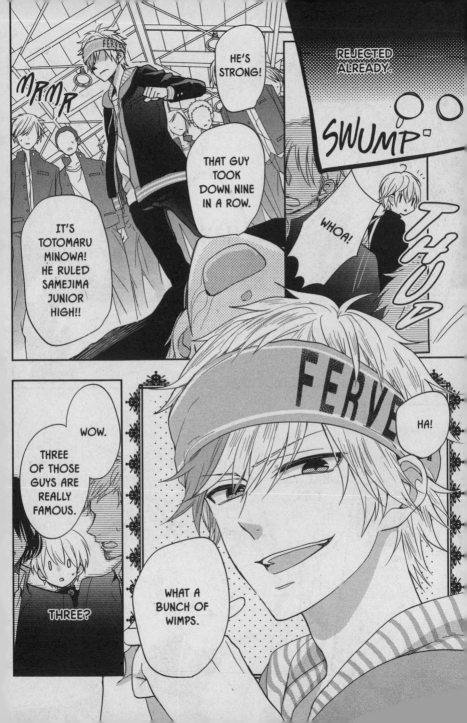

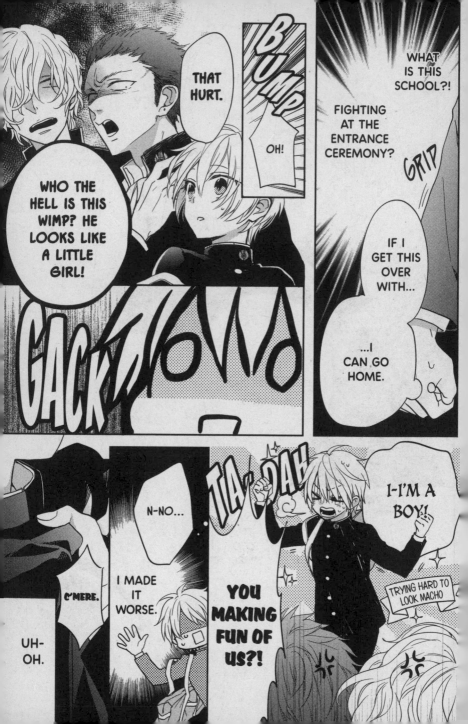

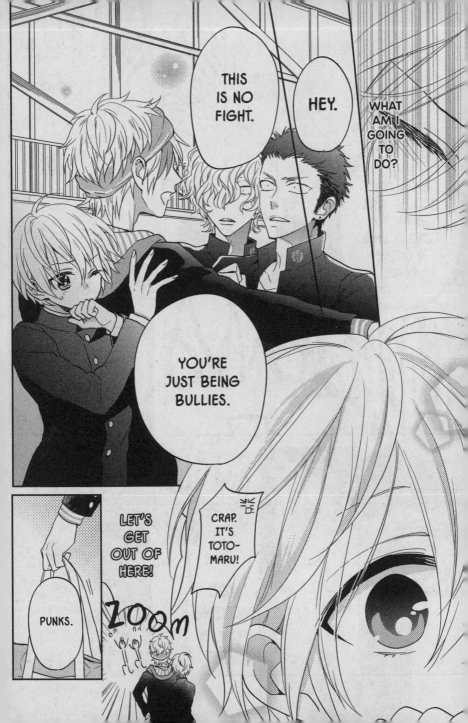

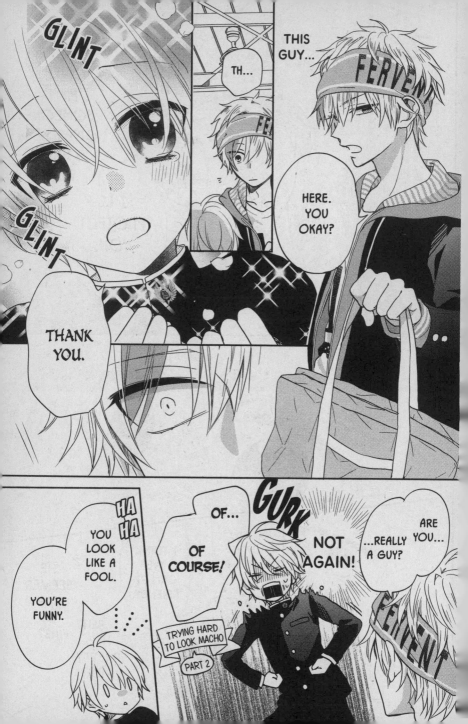

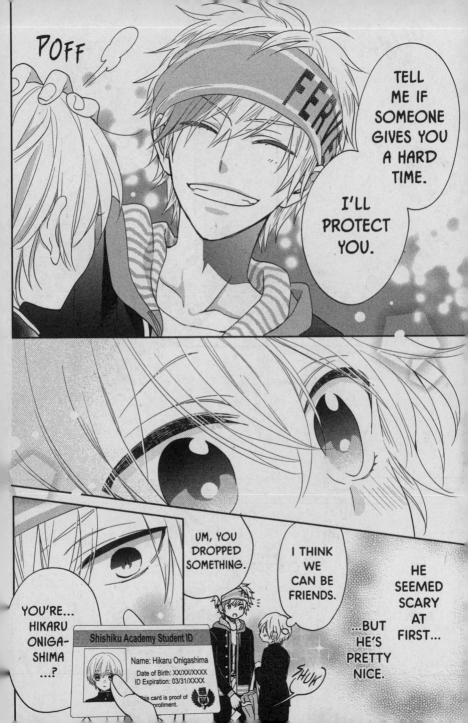

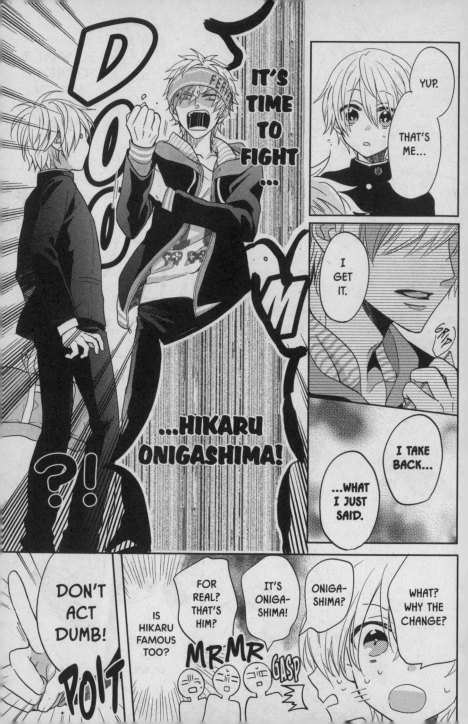

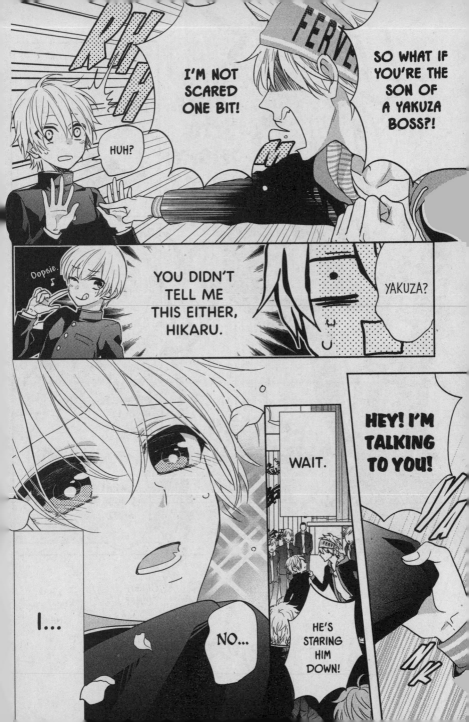

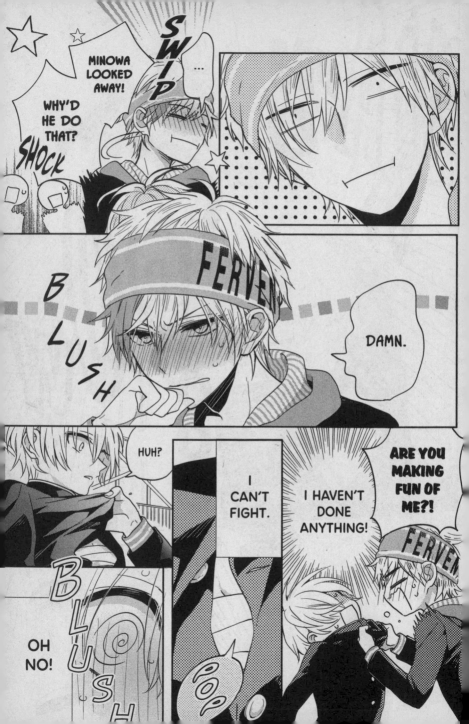

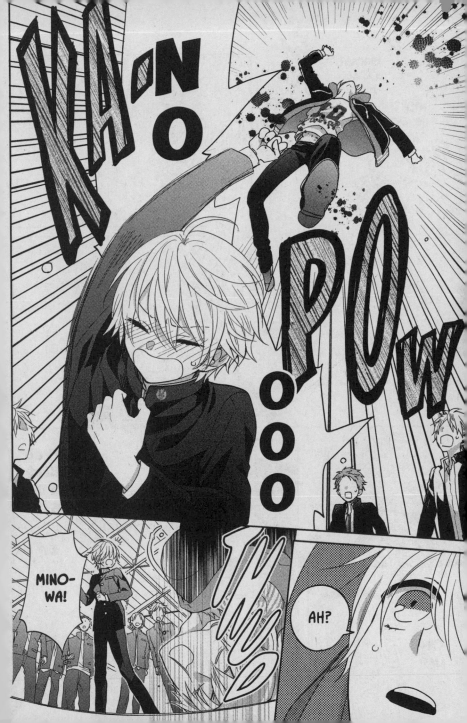

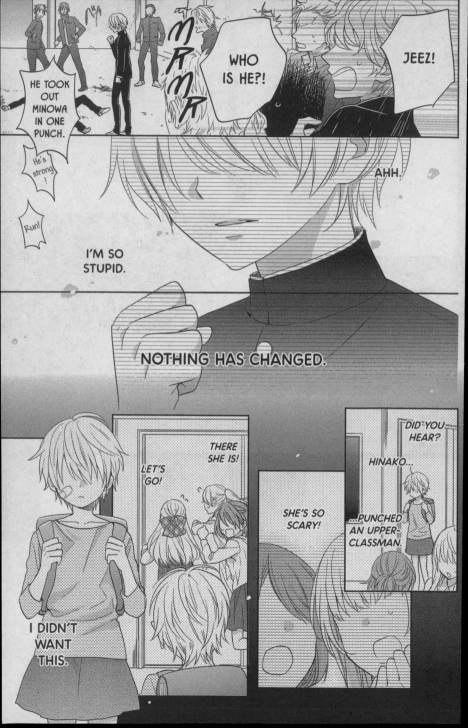

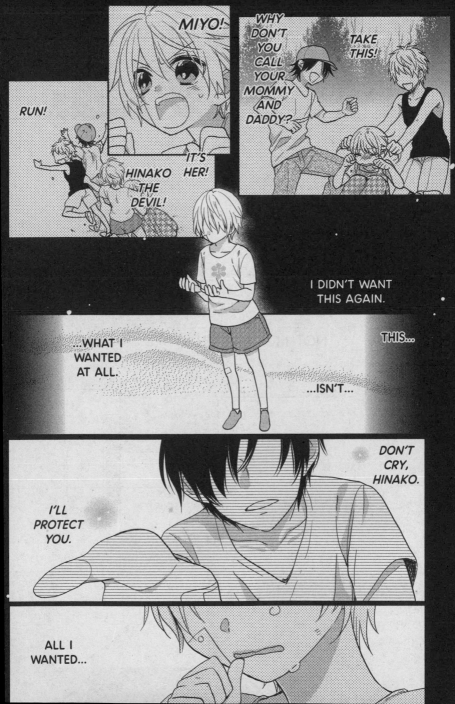

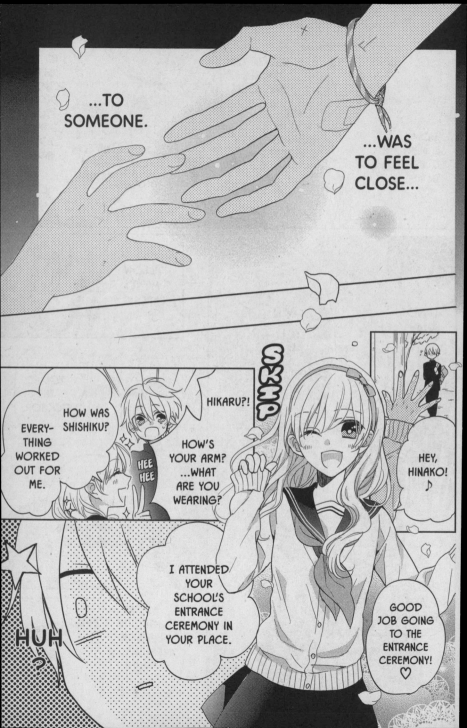

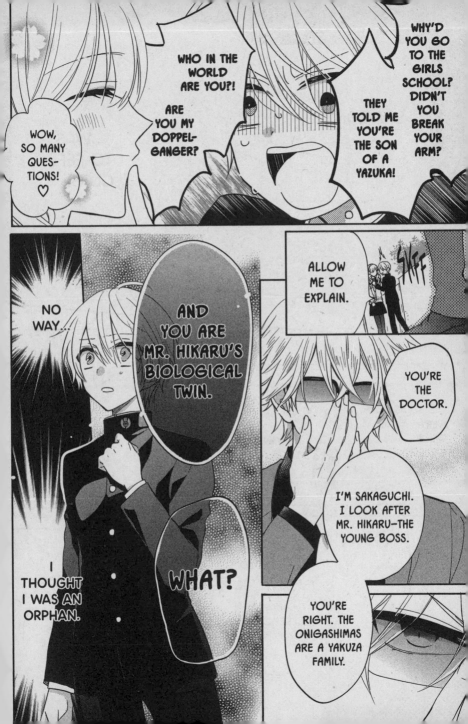

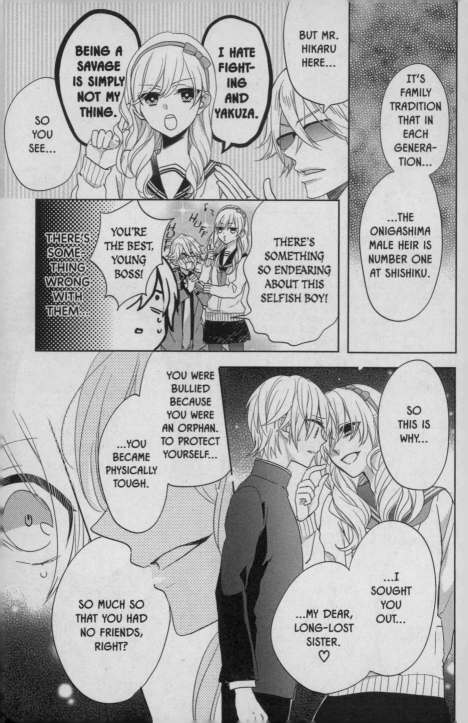

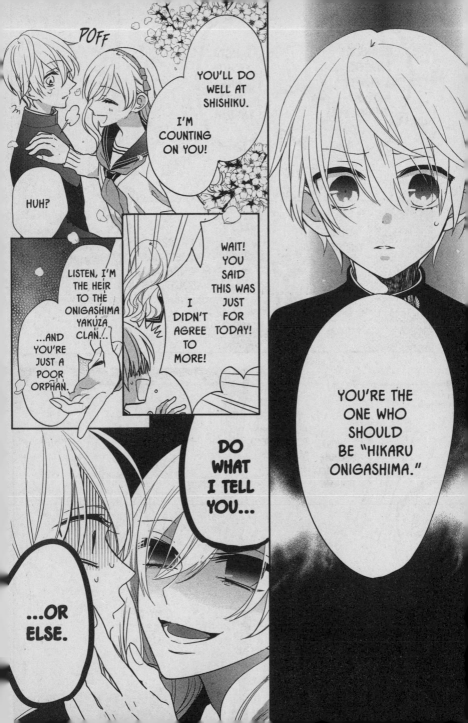

FIRST-YEAR, VIOLET CLASS

HINAKO NAKAYAMA
(FEMALE)

Height: 5'2"
Weight: 104 pounds
Blood Type: ?
Birthday: ?
Skill: Mixed Martial Arts

She has the sudden misfortune of attending a boys' school for delinquents in Hikaru's stead! I love the way she faces this challenge in her own special way. Go for it, Hinako! You're the strongest heroine (physically) ever!!

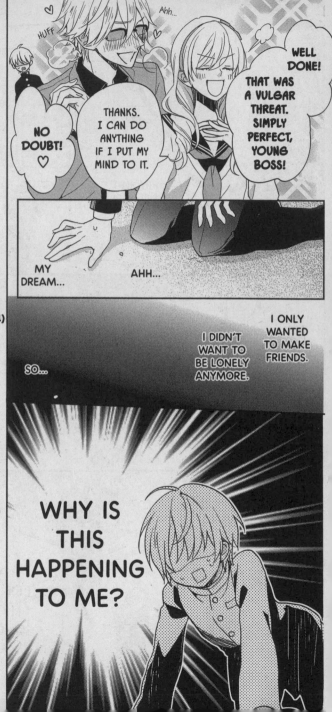

HUFF

Ahh...

WELL DONE!

THAT WAS A VULGAR THREAT. SIMPLY PERFECT, YOUNG BOSS!

NO DOUBT! ♡

THANKS. I CAN DO ANYTHING IF I PUT MY MIND TO IT.

MY DREAM...

AHH...

SO...

I DIDN'T WANT TO BE LONELY ANYMORE.

I ONLY WANTED TO MAKE FRIENDS.

WHY IS THIS HAPPENING TO ME?

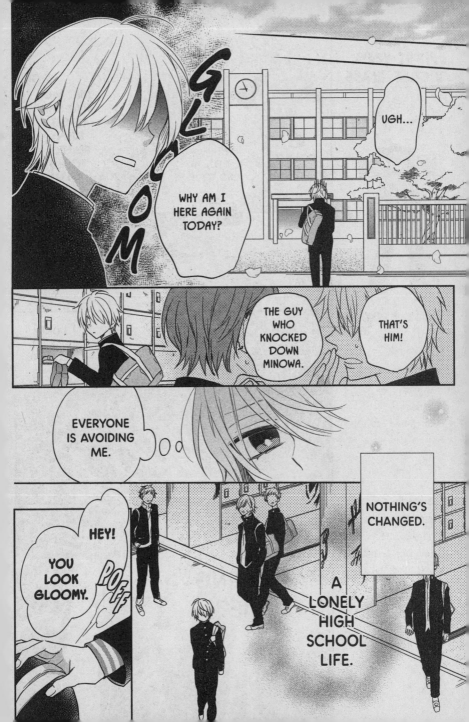

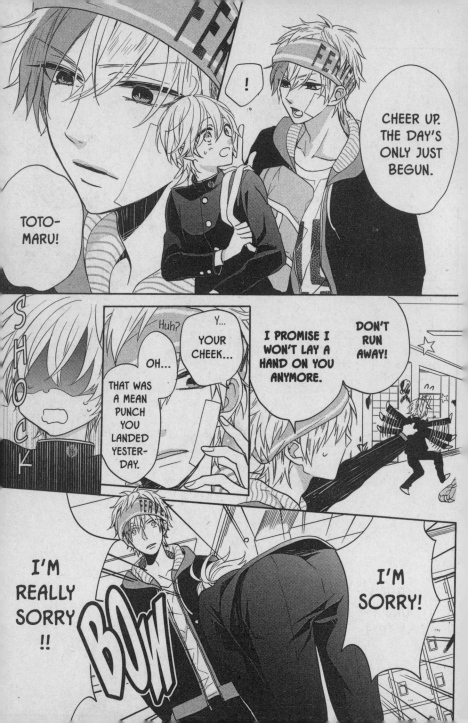

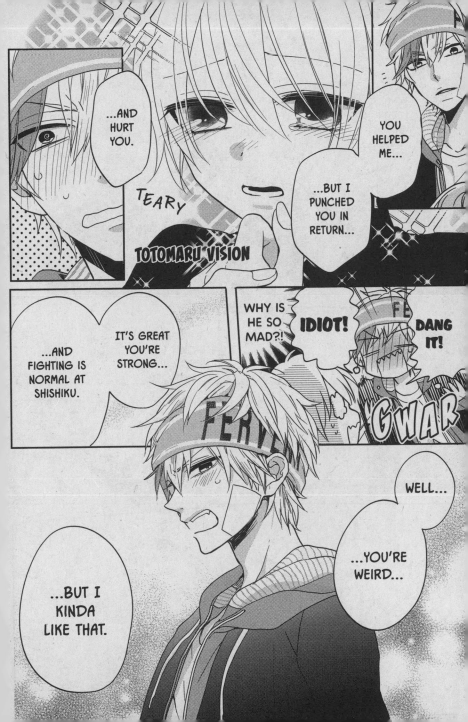

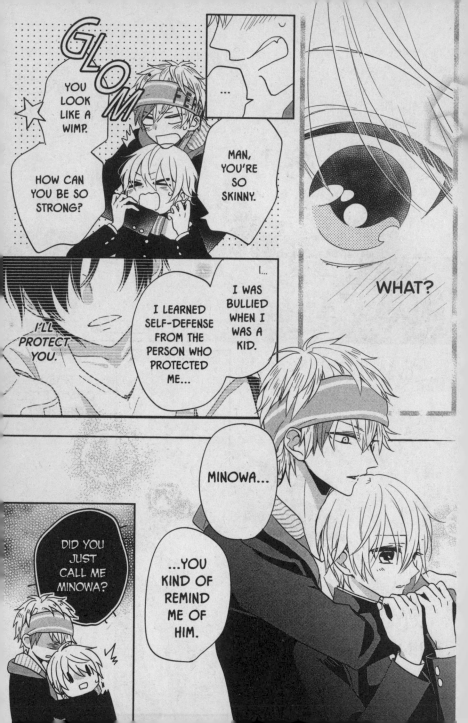

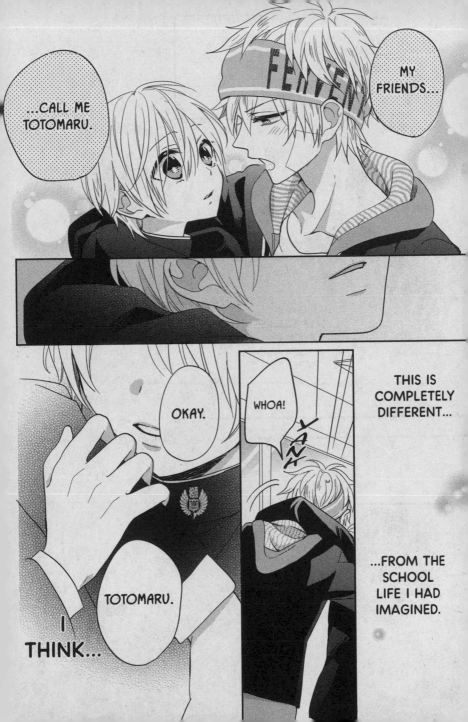

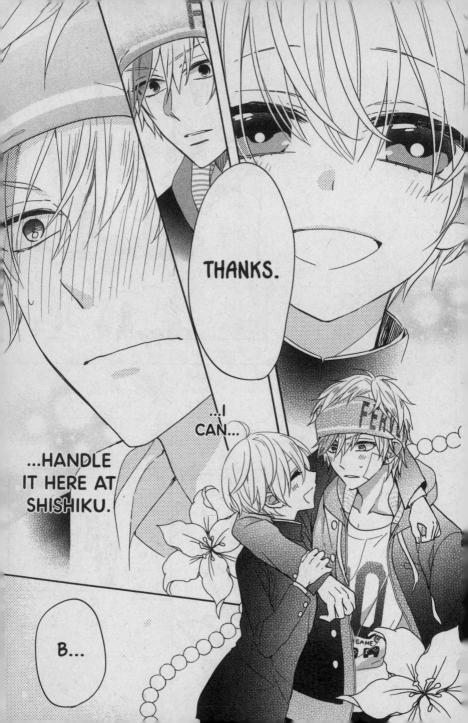

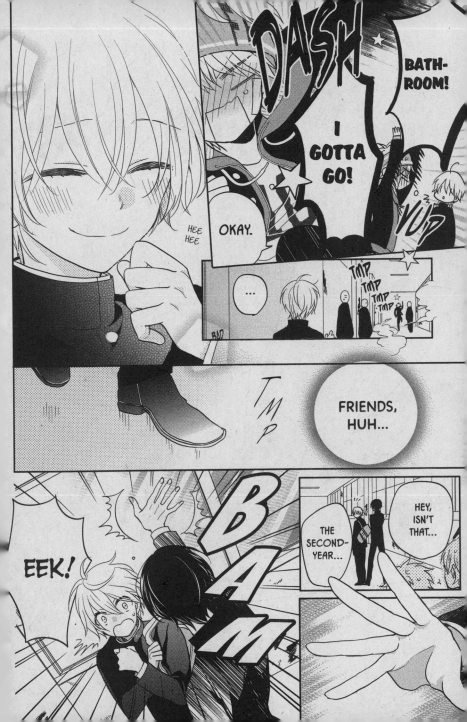

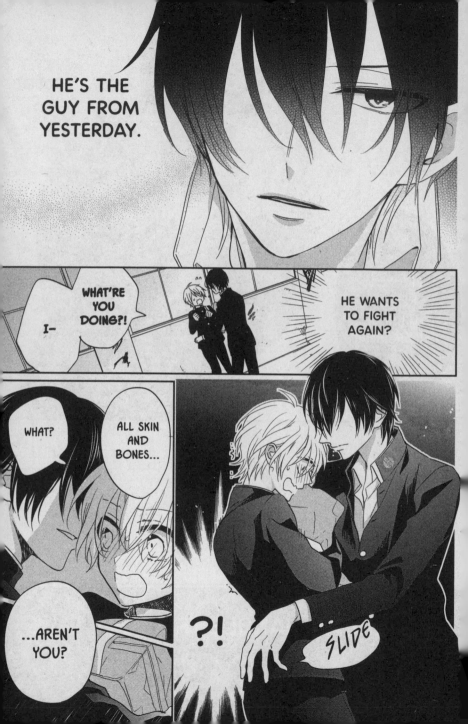

ARE YOU REALLY HIKARU ONIGASHIMA?

I DON'T THINK...

I TAKE BACK WHAT I SAID.

...I CAN HANDLE THIS LIFE!

Read more in **Kenka Bancho Otome: Love's Battle Royale** vol 1!

RWBY

Manga by Shirow Miwa
Based on the Rooster Teeth series
created by Monty Oum

The world of Remnant is filled with horrific monsters bent on the destruction of humanity. Fortunately, the kingdoms of the world have risen to combat these forces by training powerful Huntsmen and Huntresses at academies around the planet. Ruby Rose, Weiss Schnee, Blake Belladonna and Yang Xiao Long are four such Huntresses in training.

The manga includes previously unseen adventures of Team RWBY before they were teammates at Beacon Academy. Plus, a Team JNPR battle featuring a much younger Jaune!

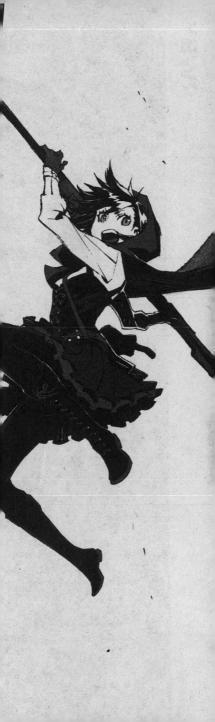

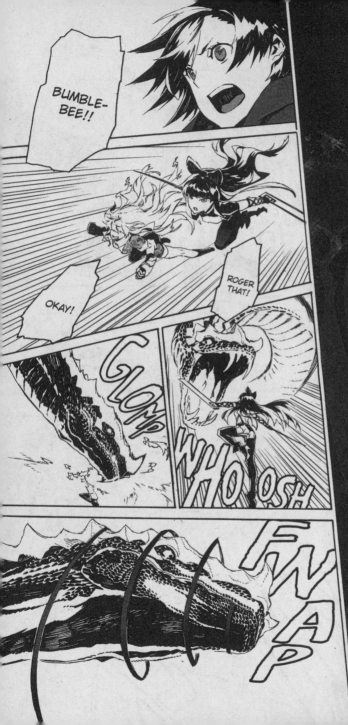

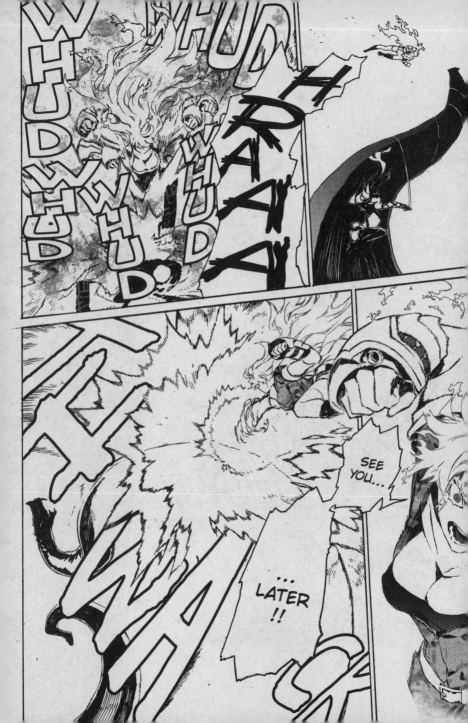

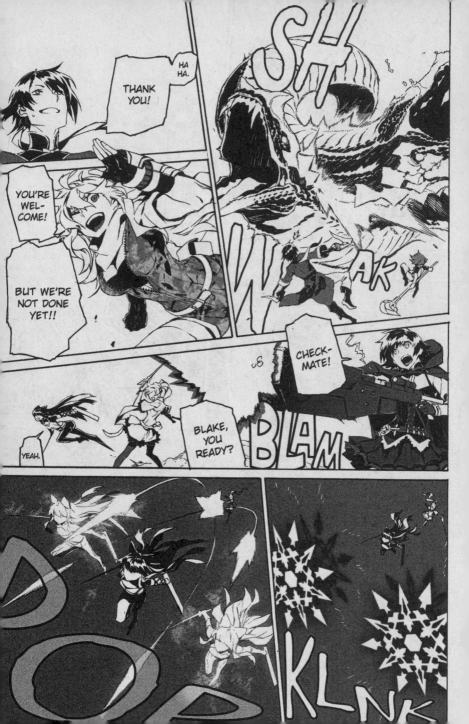

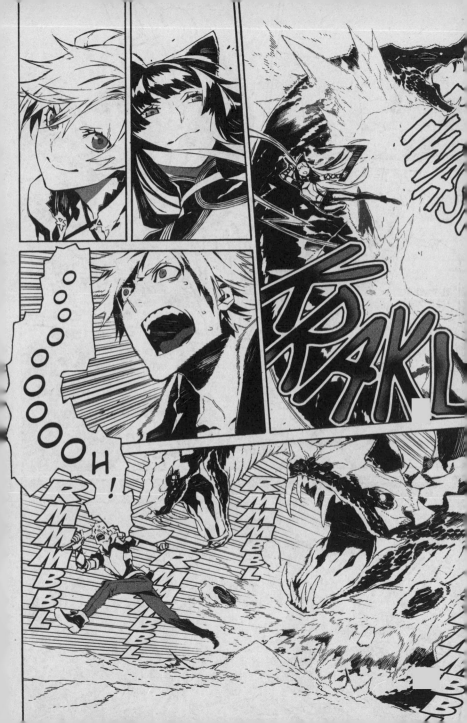

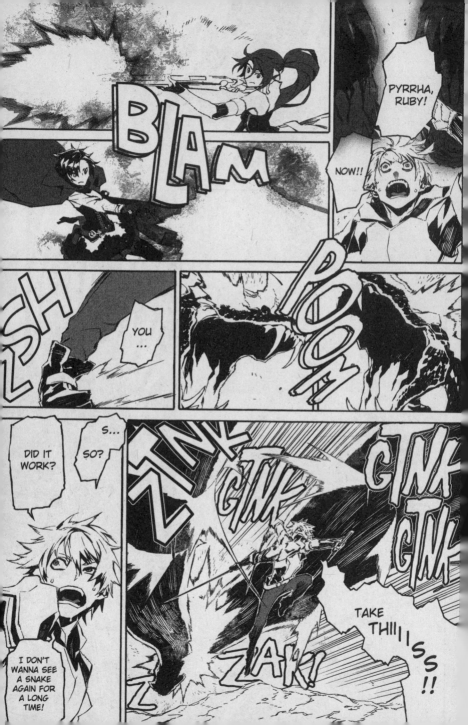

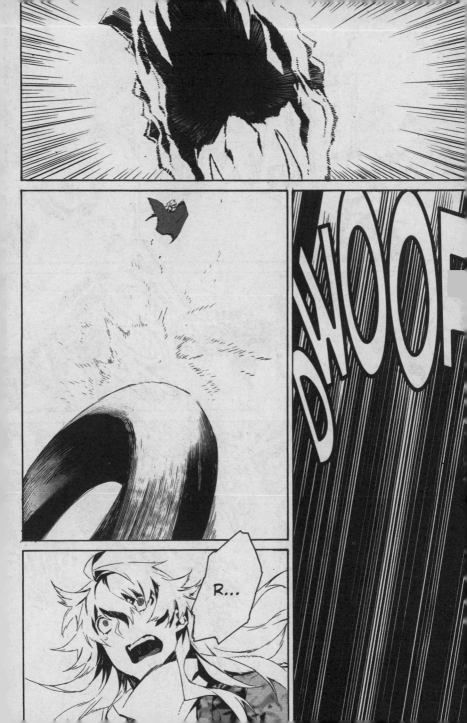

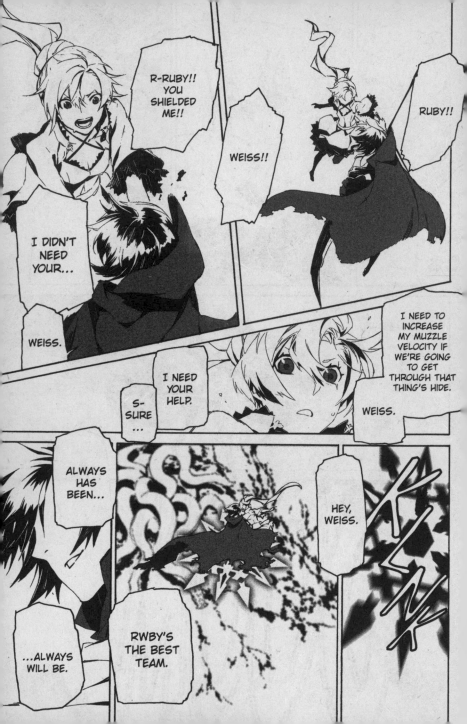

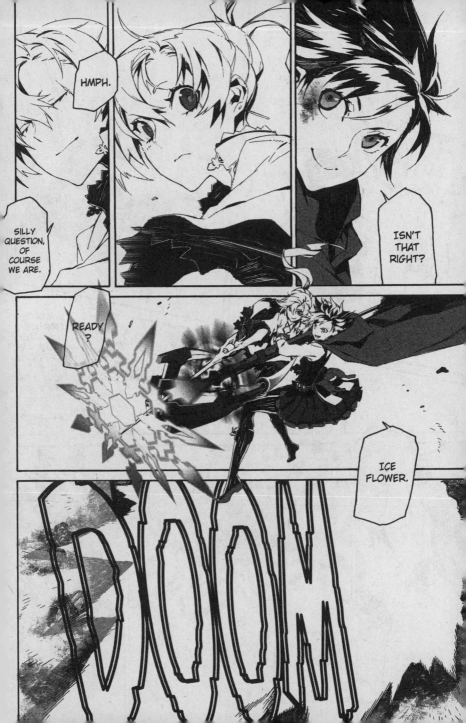

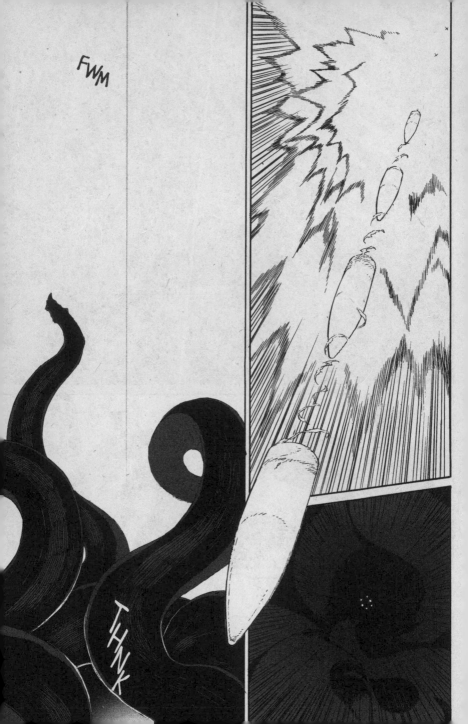

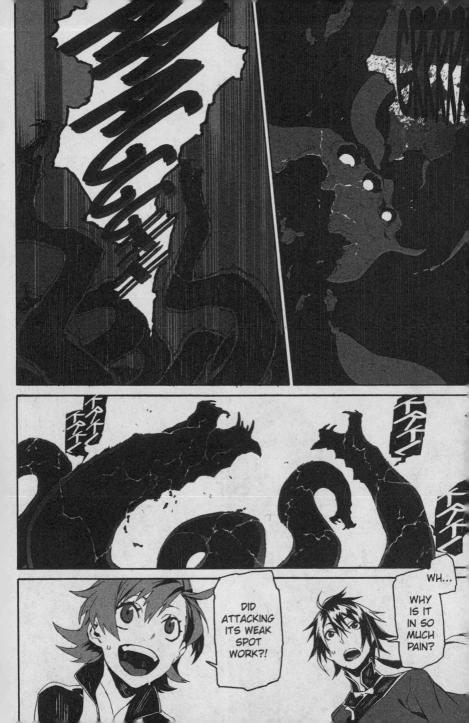

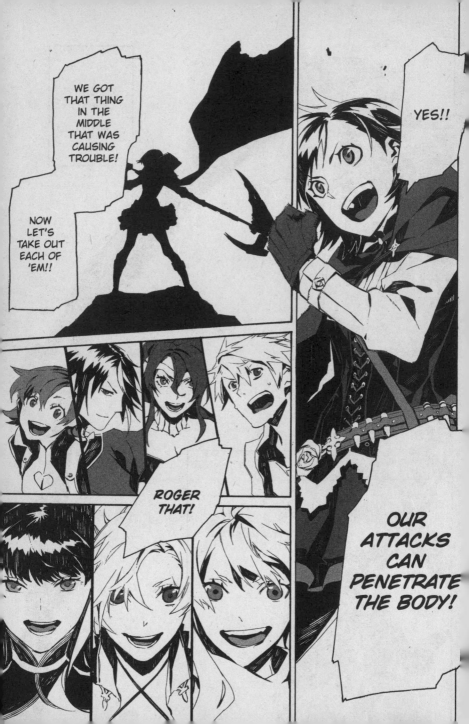

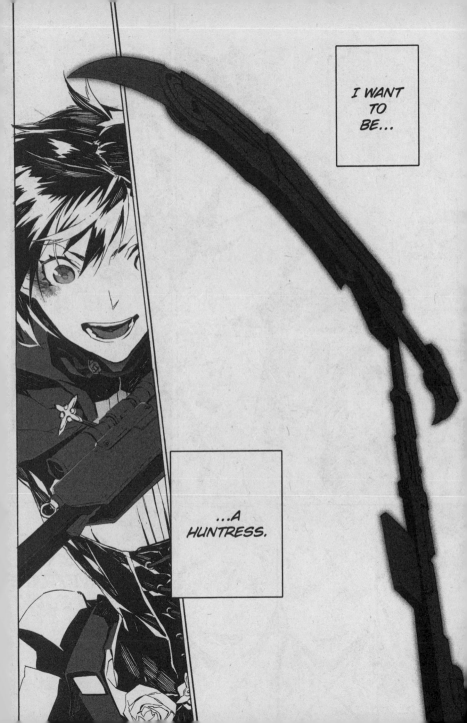

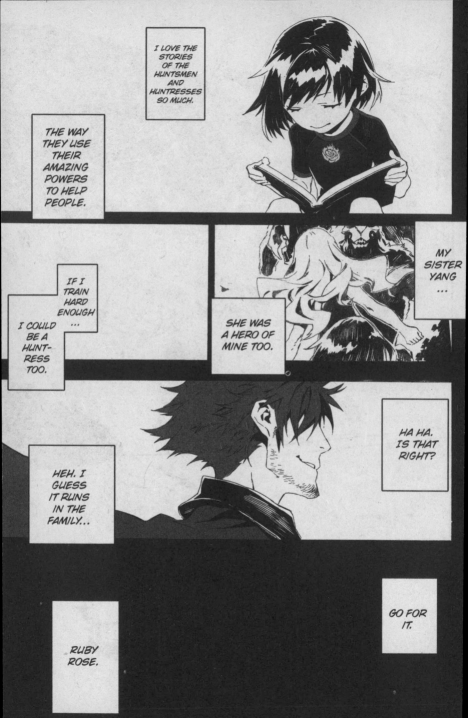

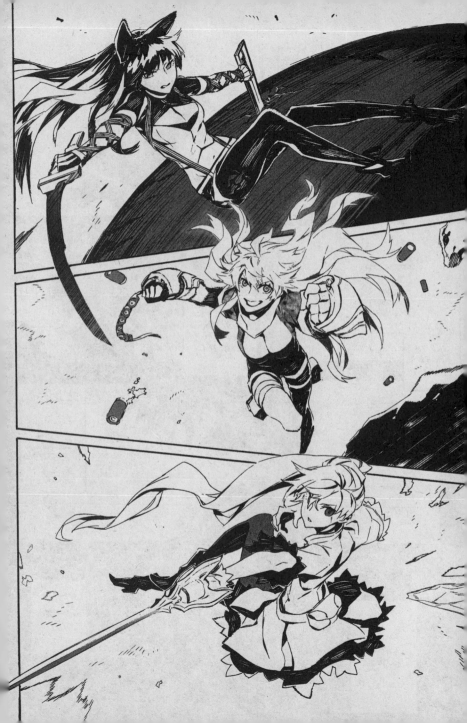

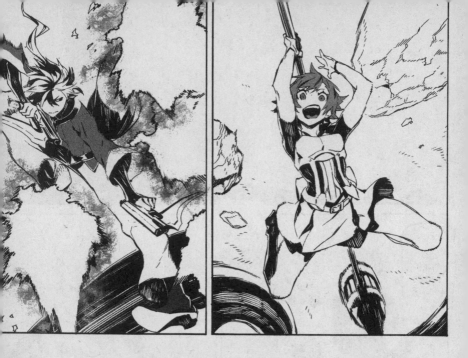

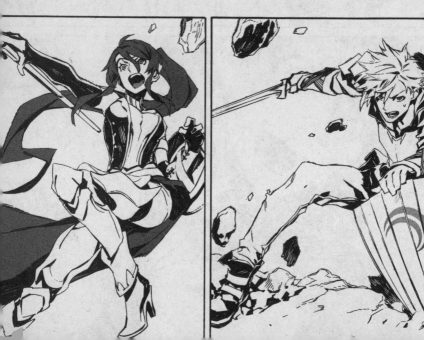

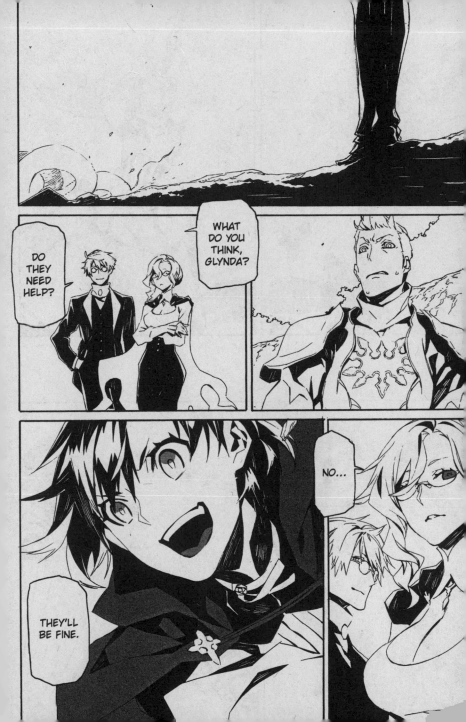

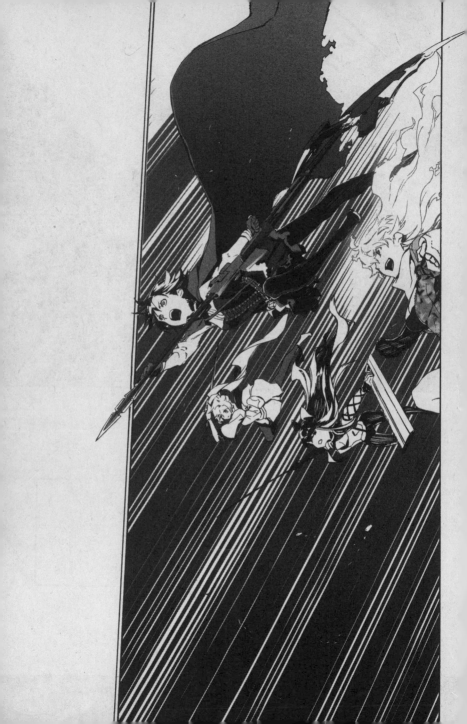

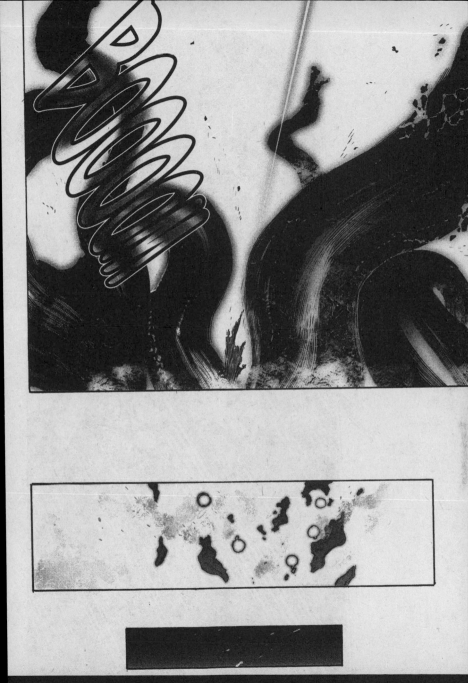

My Hero Academia: Vigilantes

Story by Hideyuki Furuhashi
Art by Betten Court
Concept by Kohei Horikoshi

Koichi Haimawari couldn't make the cut to become an official hero, so he uses his modest Quirk to do good deeds in his spare time. Then one day, a fateful encounter with some local thugs leads him to team up with two other unlikely heroes. None of them really know what they're doing, but they've got the courage—or foolishness—to try. But they soon discover fighting evil takes more than just being brave...

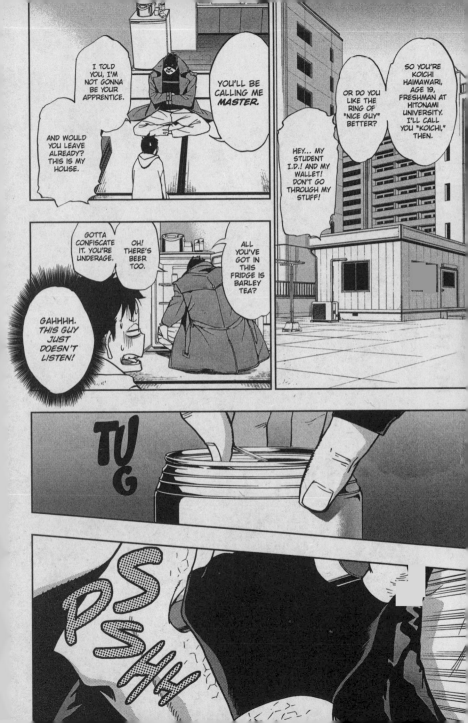

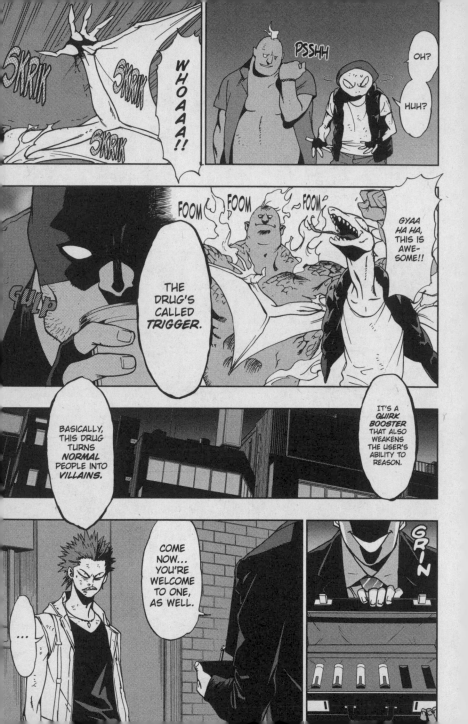

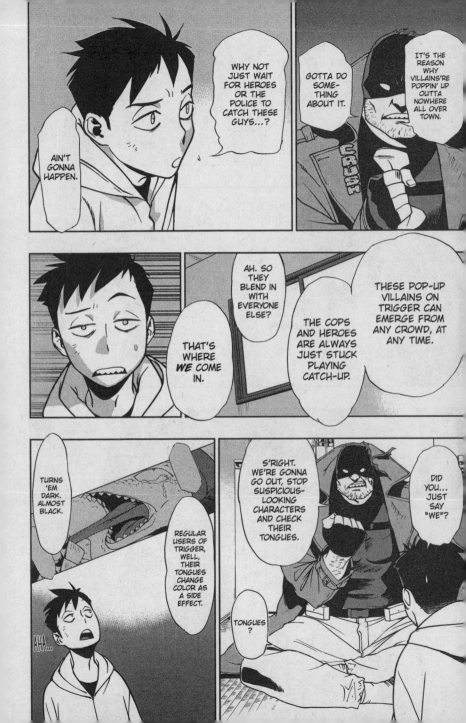

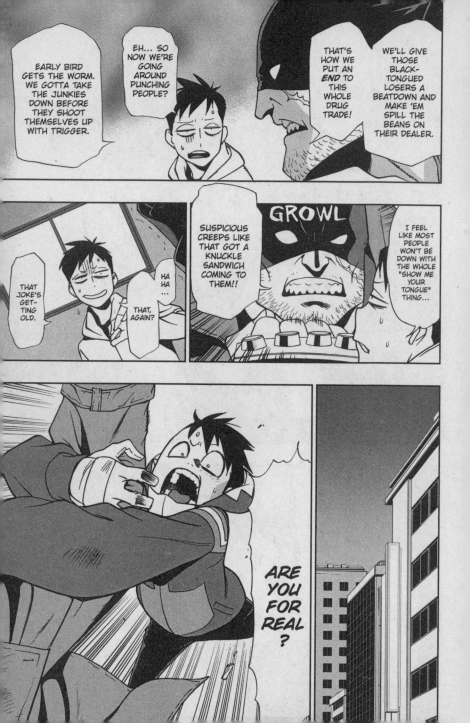

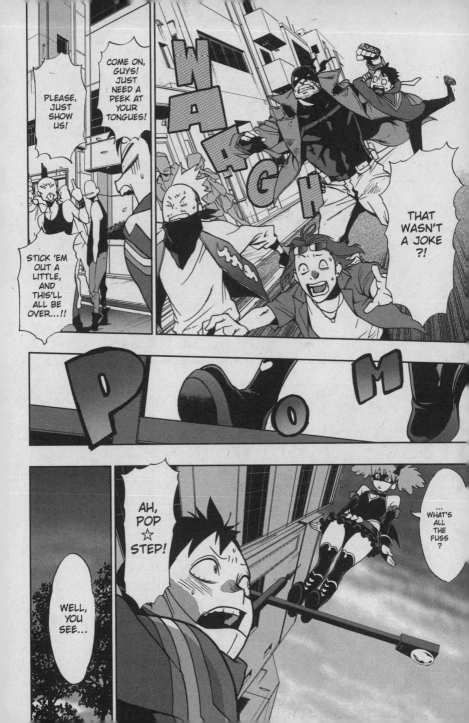

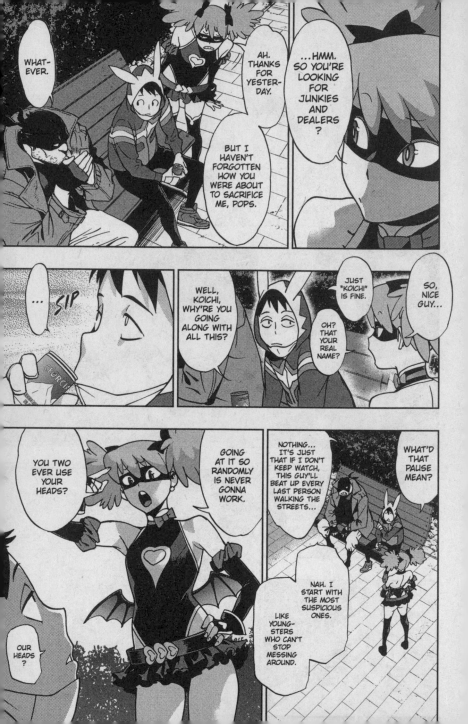

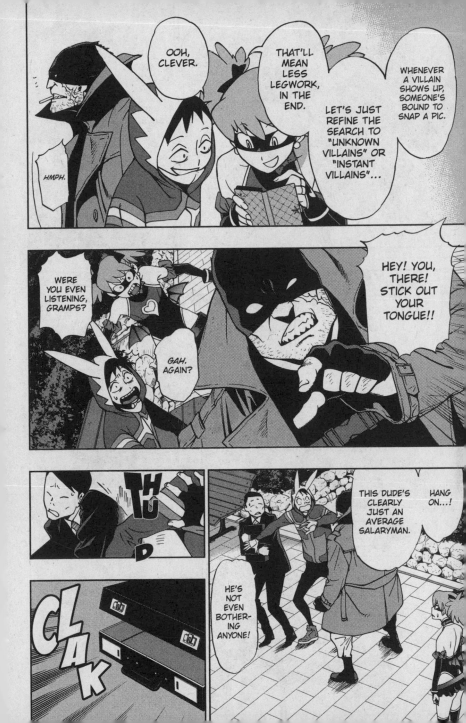

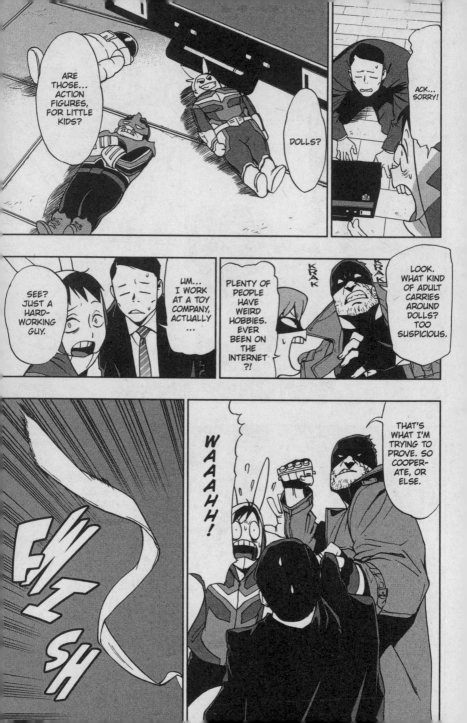

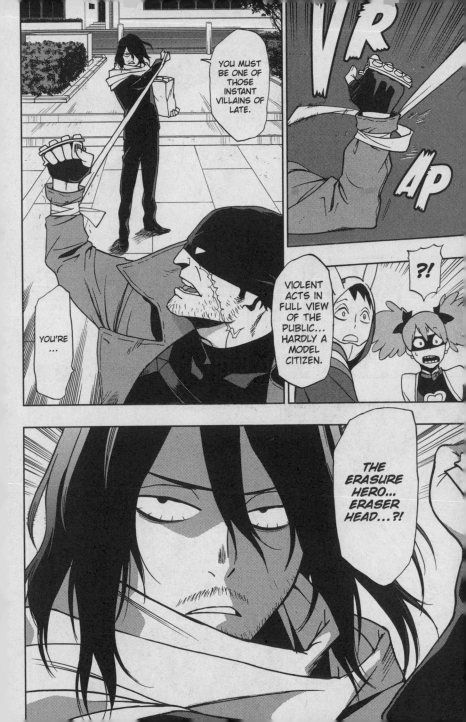

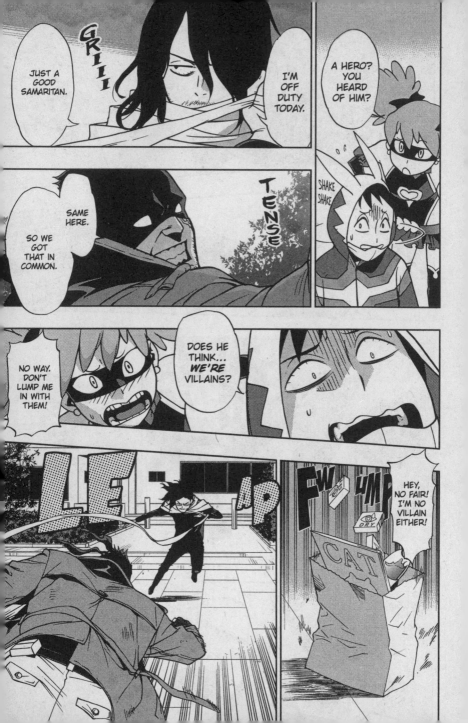

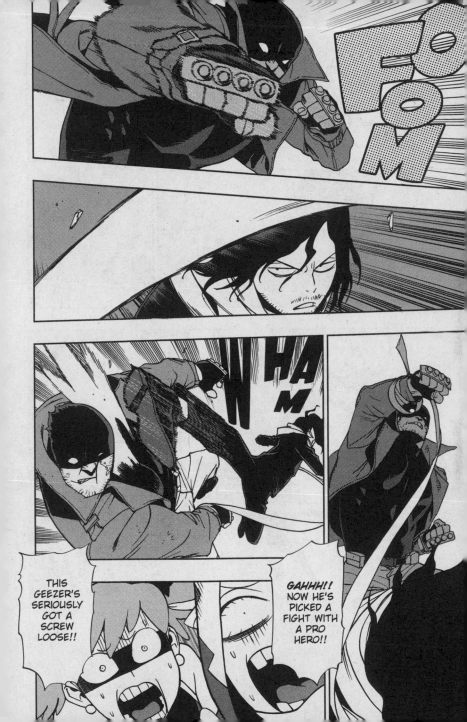

FLYING

MUST BE THE TYPE TO PUSH PAST THE PAIN WITH A DURABILITY-BASED QUIRK?

BUT IT'S A FOOL'S ERRAND, TAKING ME ON LIKE THIS...

TMP

NOT RATIONAL AT ALL!!

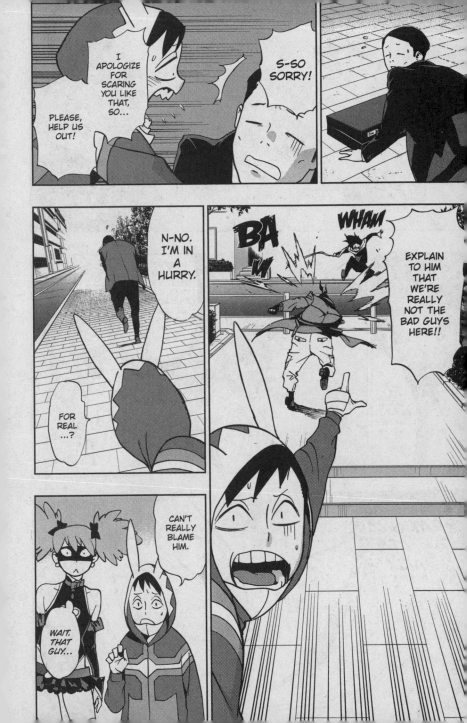

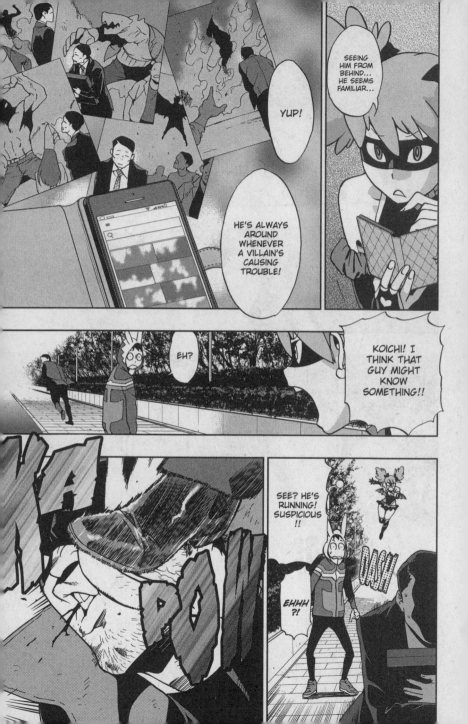

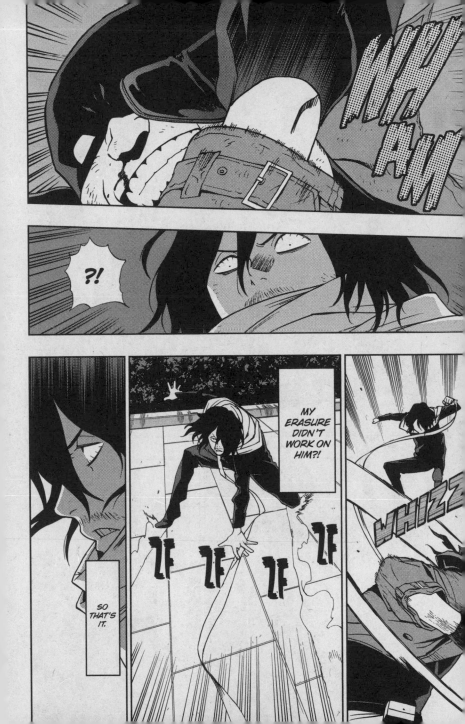

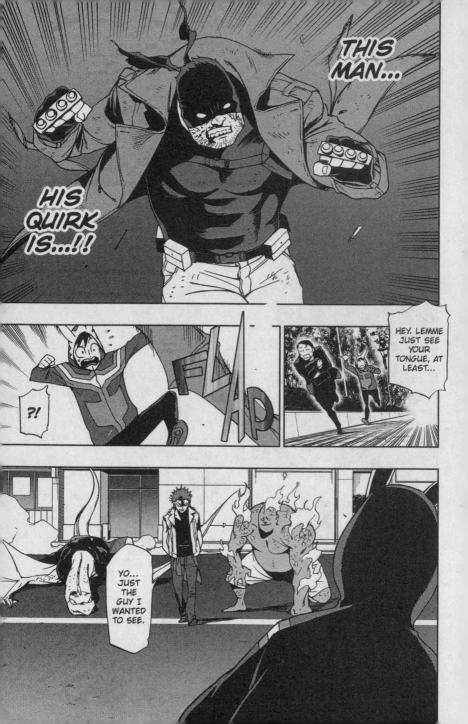

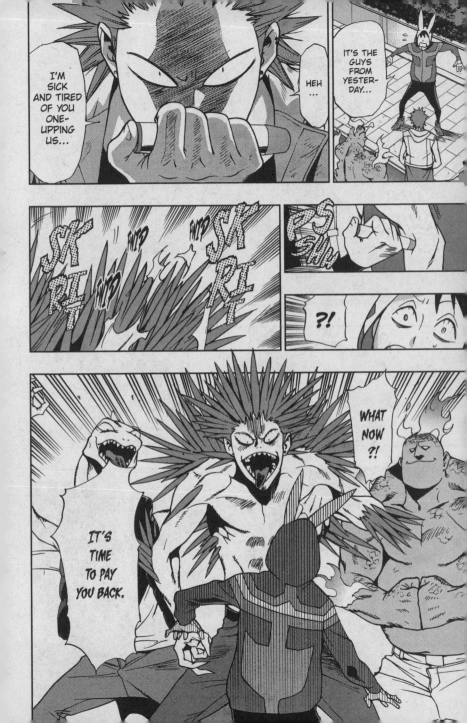

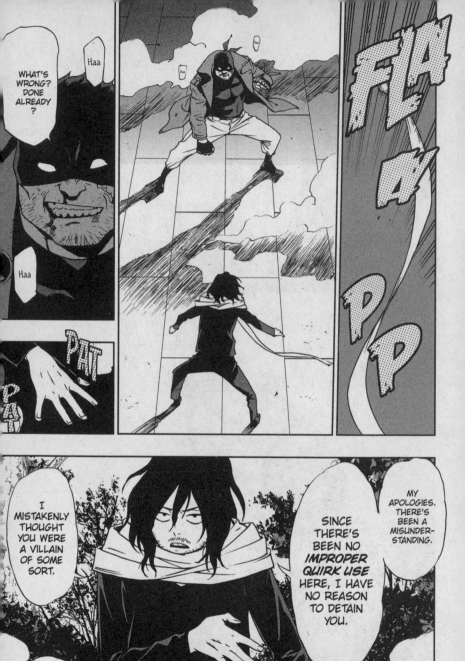

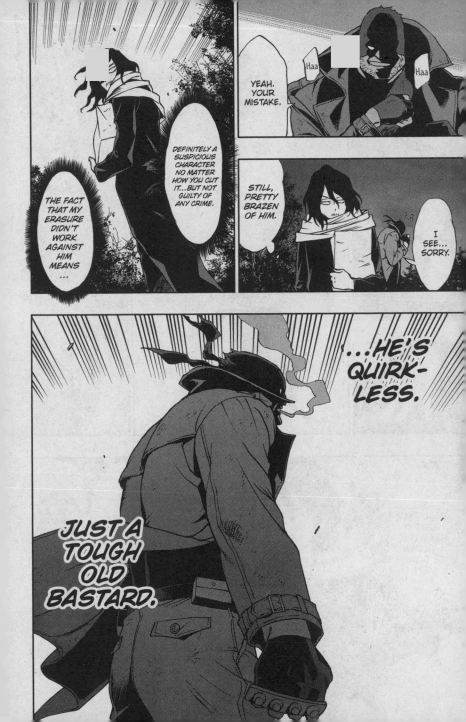

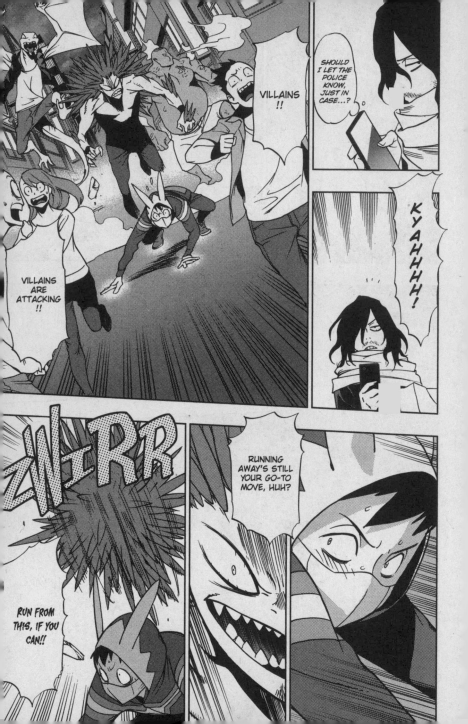

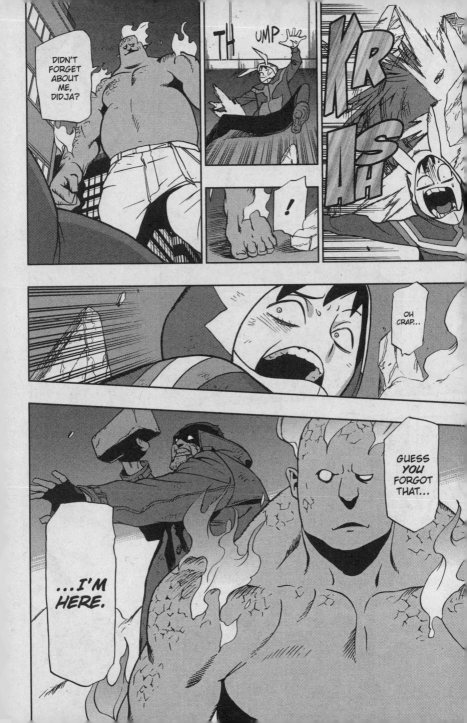

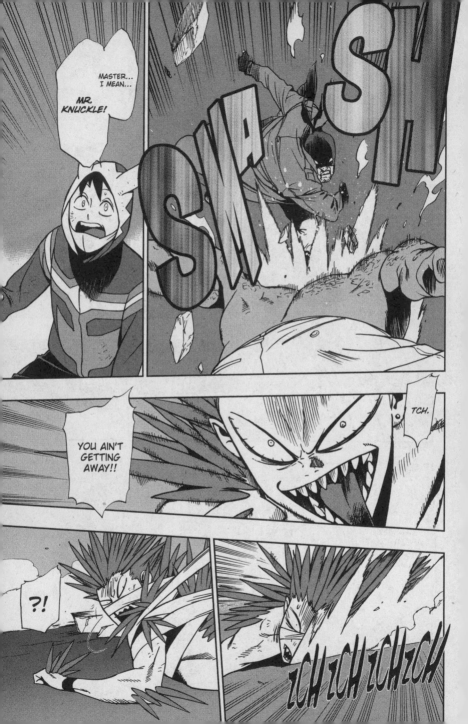

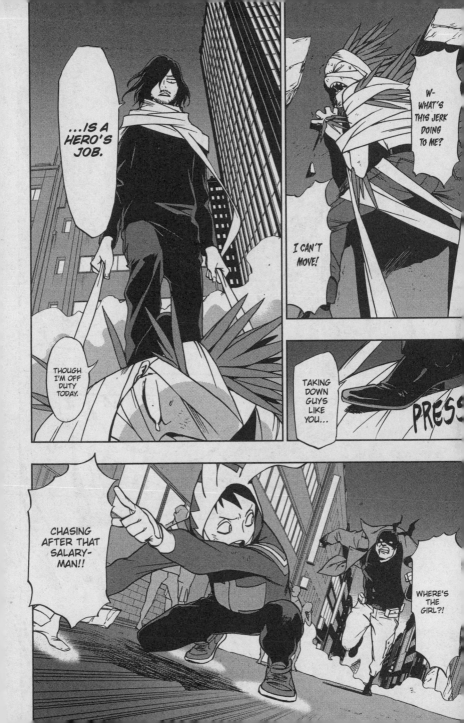

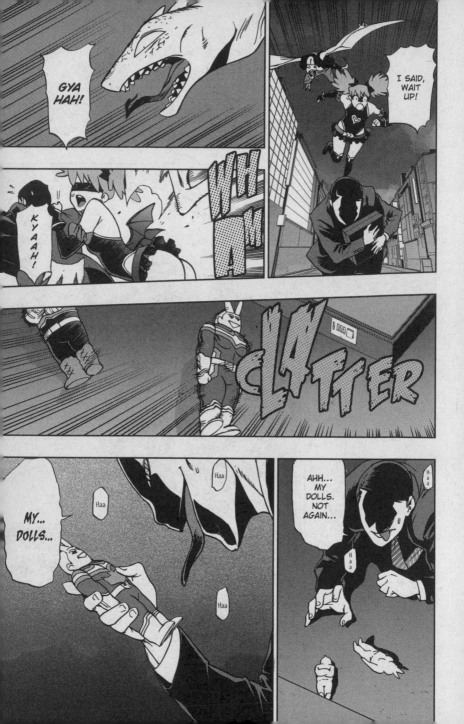

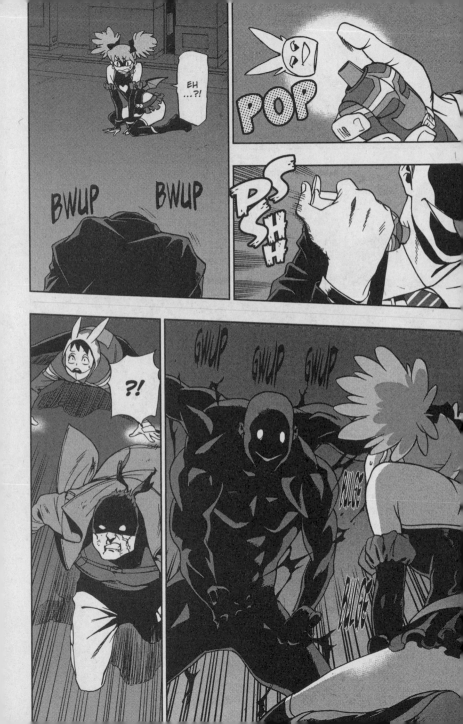

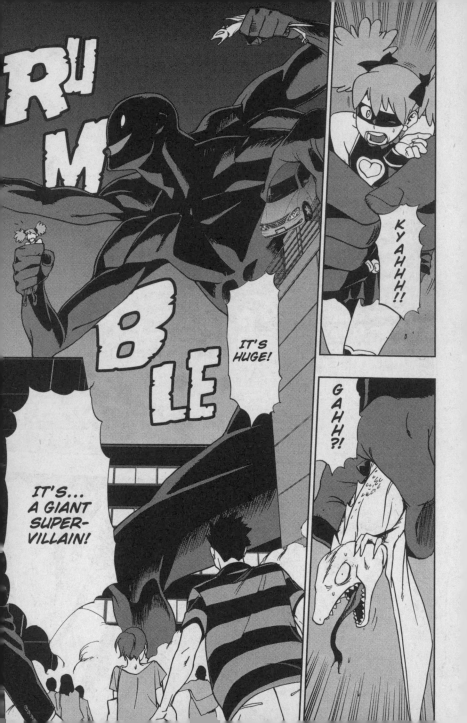

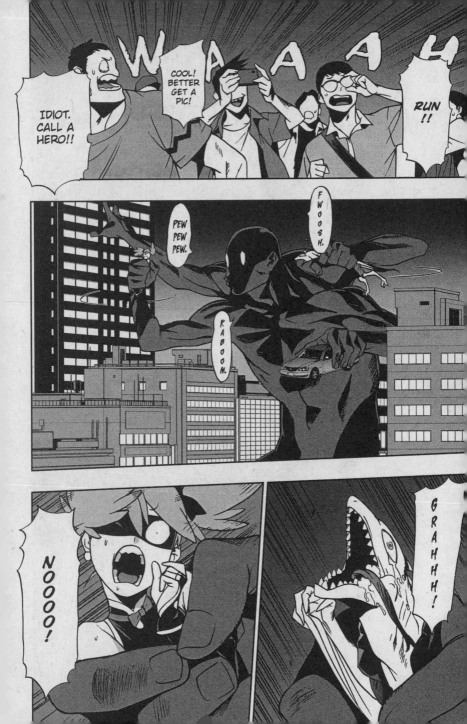

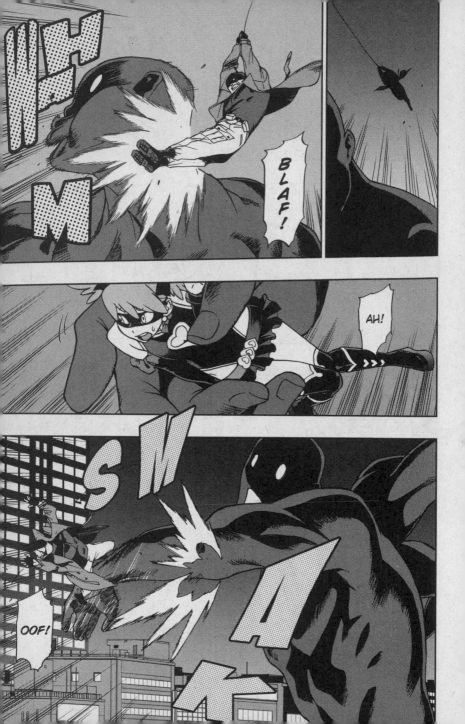

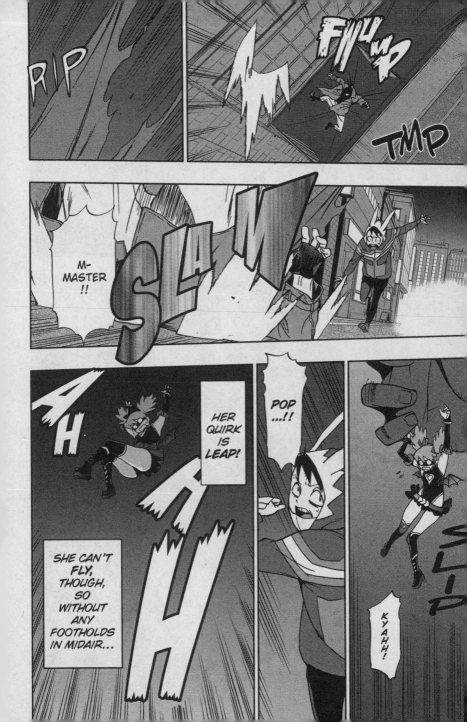

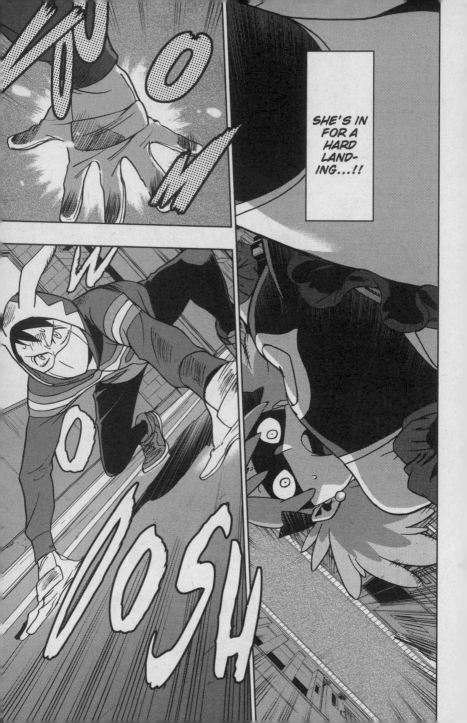

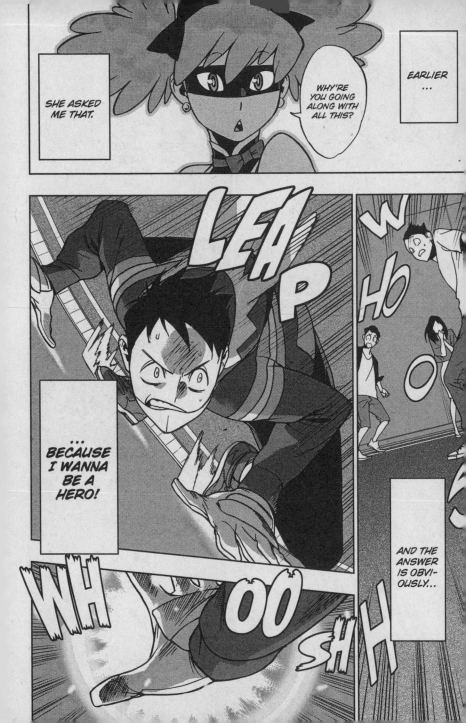

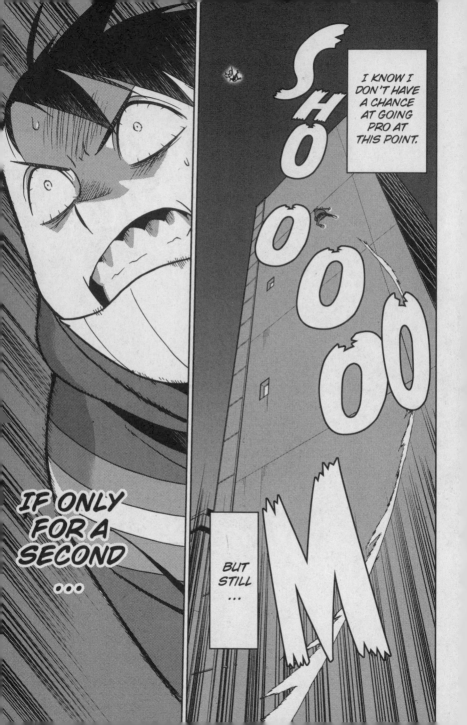

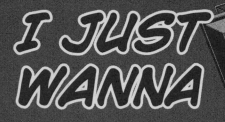

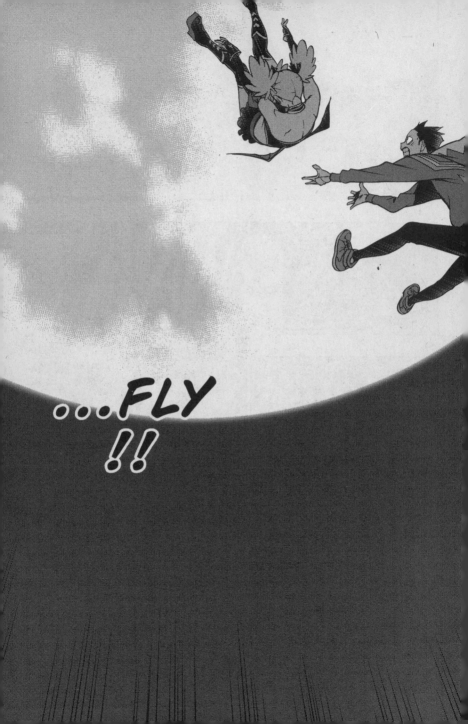

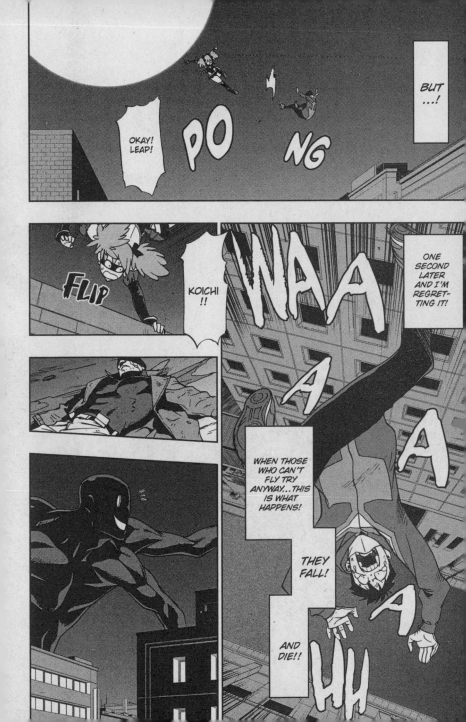

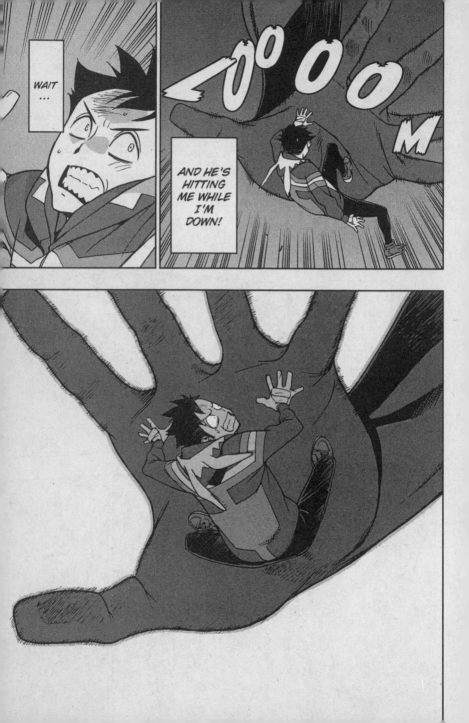

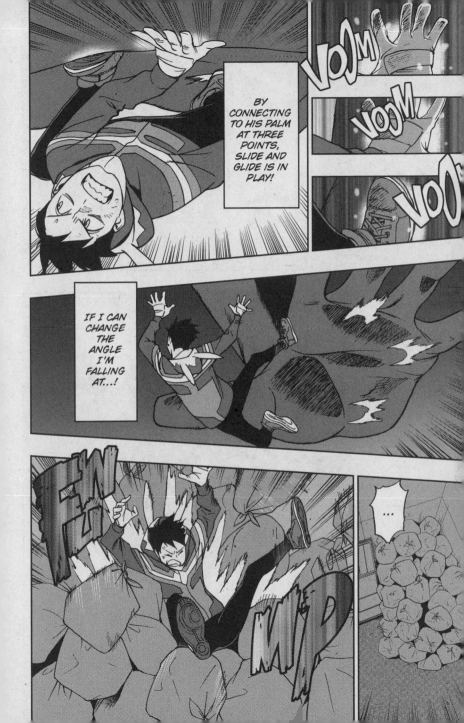

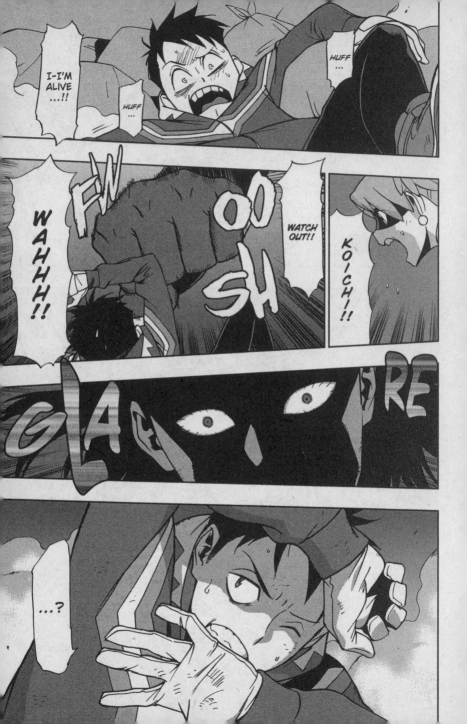

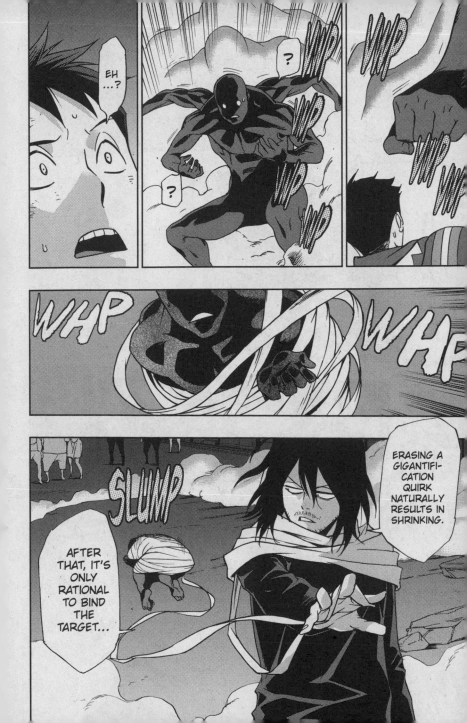

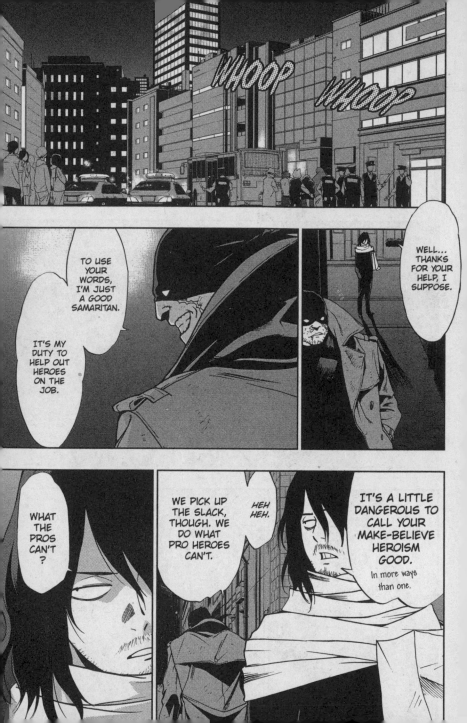

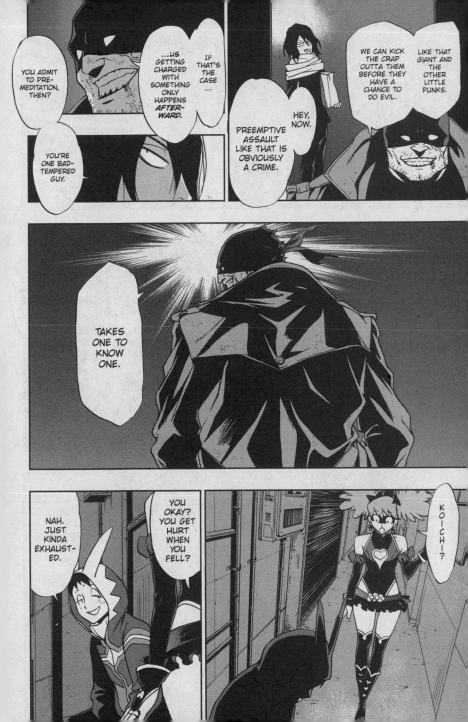

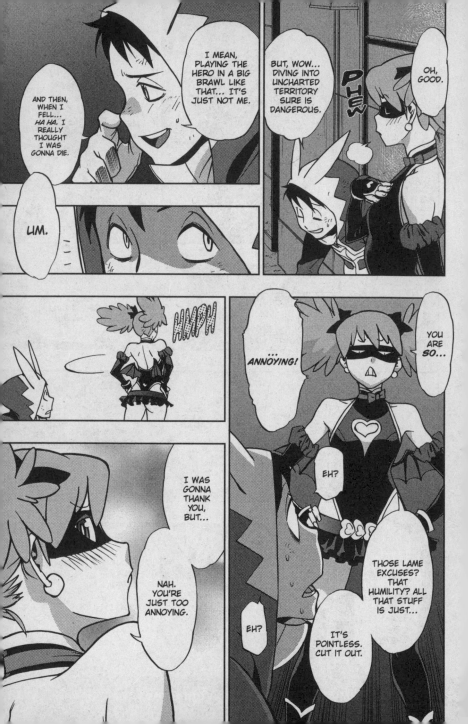

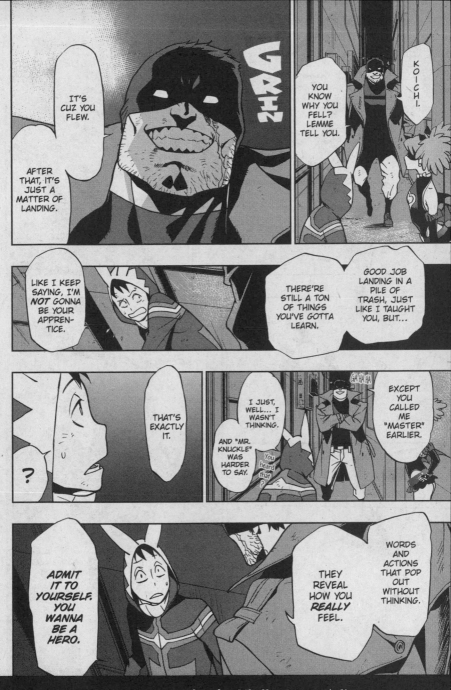

Demon Slayer: Kimetsu no Yaiba

Story and Art by Koyoharu Gotouge

In Taisho-era Japan, kindhearted Tanjiro Kamado makes a living selling charcoal. But his peaceful life is shattered when a demon slaughters his entire family. His little sister Nezuko is the only survivor, but she has been transformed into a demon herself! Tanjiro sets out on a dangerous journey to find a way to return his sister to normal and destroy the demon who ruined his life.

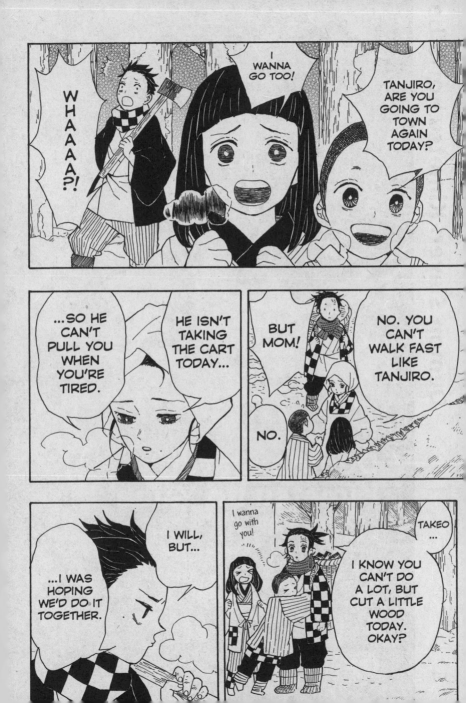

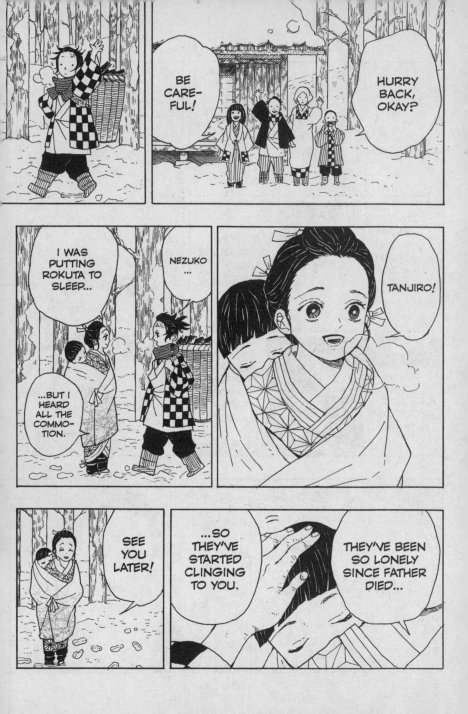

OUR LIFE ISN'T EASY, BUT WE'RE HAPPY.

IT'S ALWAYS CHANGING.

BUT LIFE IS LIKE THE WEATHER...

...AND THE SNOW WON'T ALWAYS KEEP FALLING.

IT WON'T ALWAYS BE EASY...

...THE SMELL OF BLOOD IN THE AIR.

WHEN HAPPINESS ENDS THERE'S ALWAYS...

OH, TANJIRO!

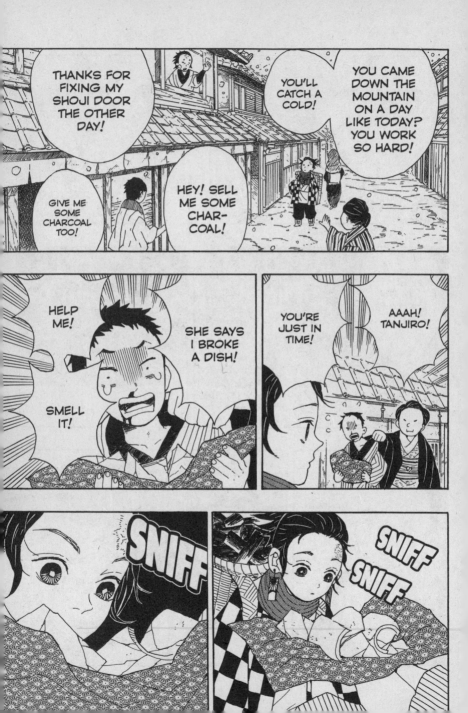

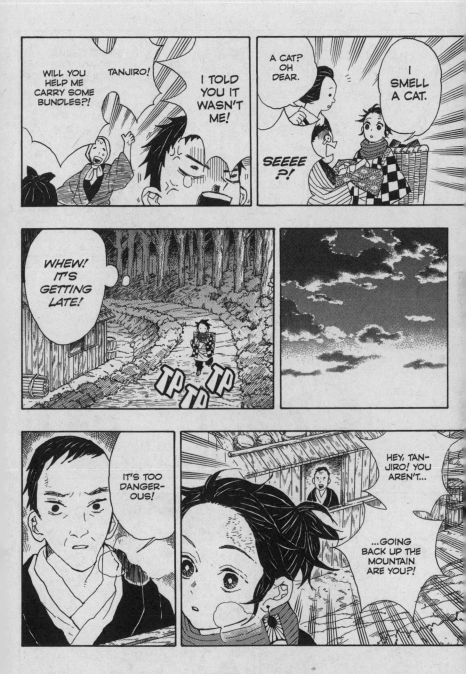

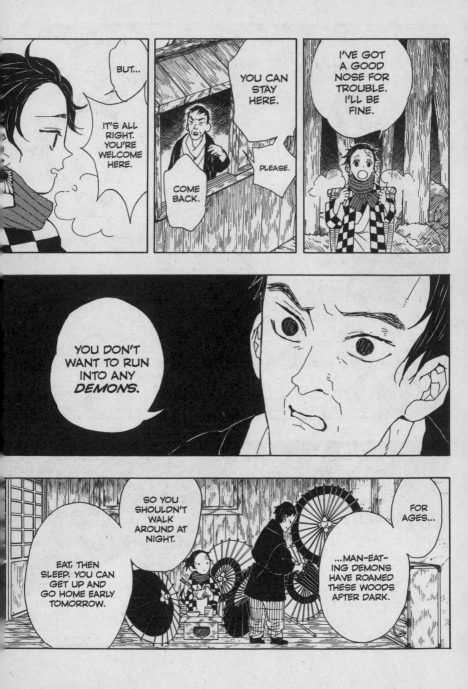

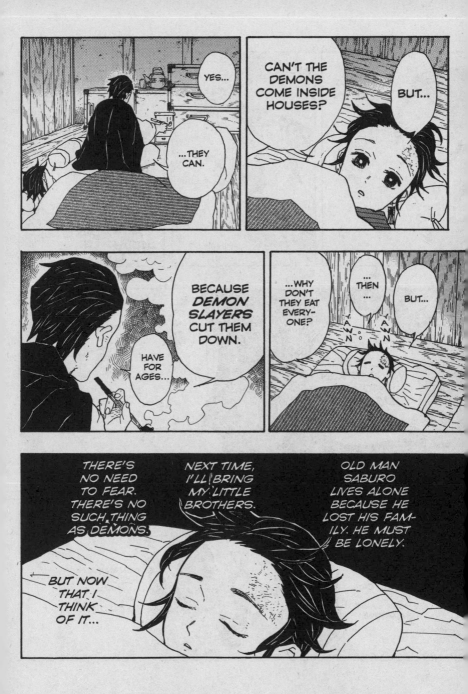

...MY GRANDMOTHER SAID THE SAME THING BEFORE SHE DIED.

WHEN HAPPINESS ENDS THERE'S ALWAYS...

...THE SMELL OF BLOOD IN THE AIR.

HFF

HFF

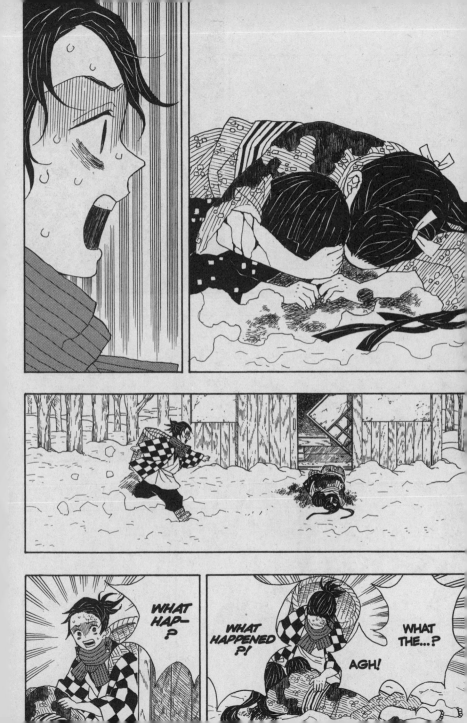

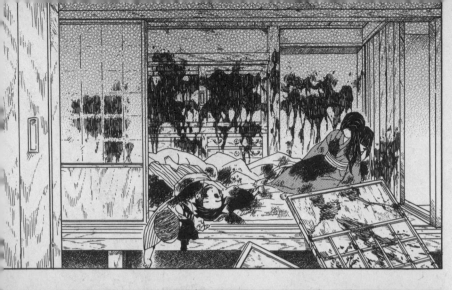

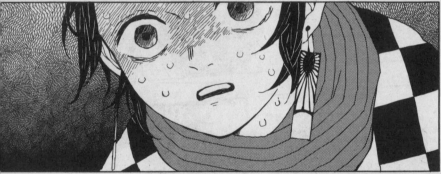

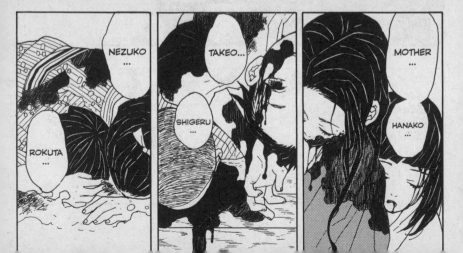

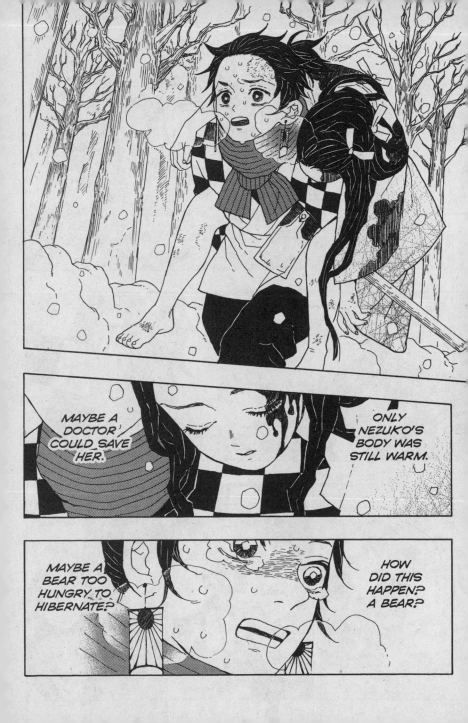

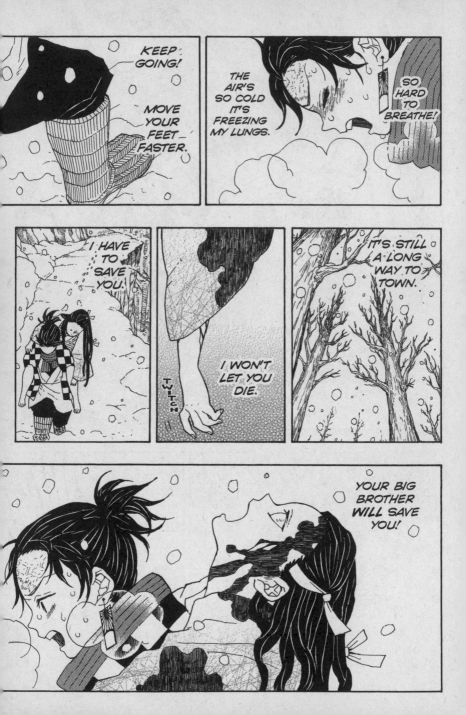

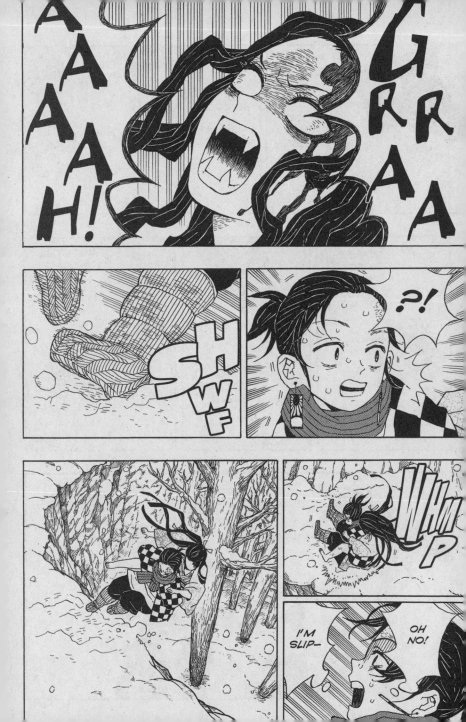

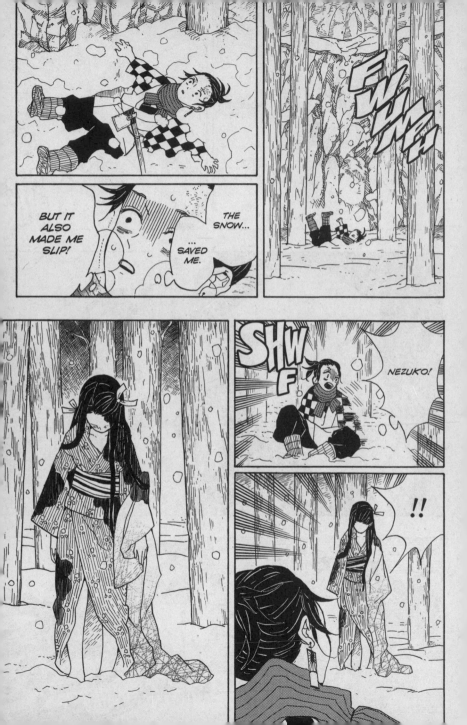

YOU SHOULDN'T BE UP!

...CARRY YOU INTO TOWN!

LET ME...

NEZUKO!

ARE YOU ALL RIGHT?

SHF

NEZUKO ...

WHUMPH

OMP

CH

I THOUGHT OF WHAT OLD MAN SABURO SAID.

A DEMON!

WAS NEZUKO...

...A MAN-EATING DEMON?

NEZUKO HAS BEEN HUMAN...

...SINCE THE DAY SHE WAS BORN.

NO, THAT WAS IM-POSSIBLE.

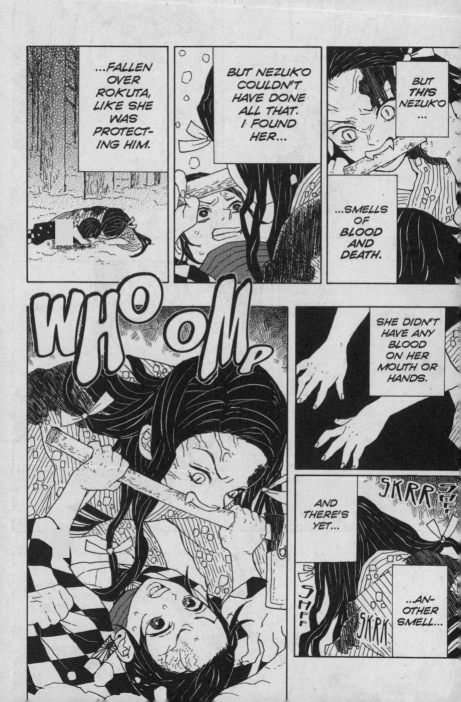

...AND SHE'S GETTING STRONGER!

...SHE'S GROWING BIGGER...

WHATEVER THE REASON...

...HAPPENED TO MY WHOLE FAMILY.

WHILE I WAS SAFELY ASLEEP IN TOWN, SOMETHING HORRIBLE...

BUT SHE'S SO STRONG! I CAN'T PUSH HER AWAY!

NEZUKO!

I HAVE TO SAVE NEZUKO IF I CAN!

HOW THEY MUST HAVE SUFFERED.

...AND I WASN'T THERE TO HELP THEM.

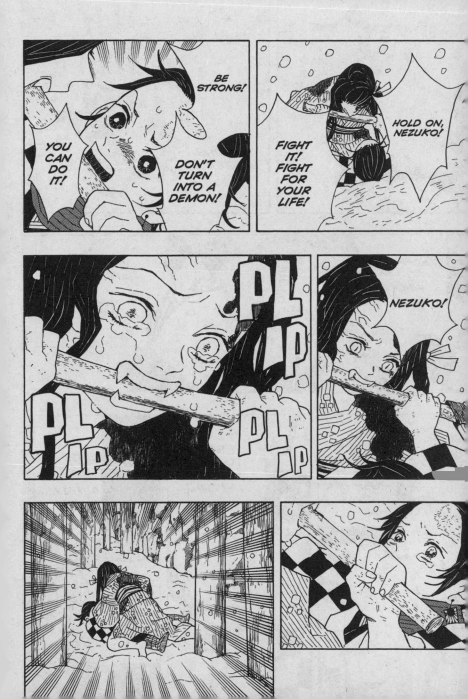

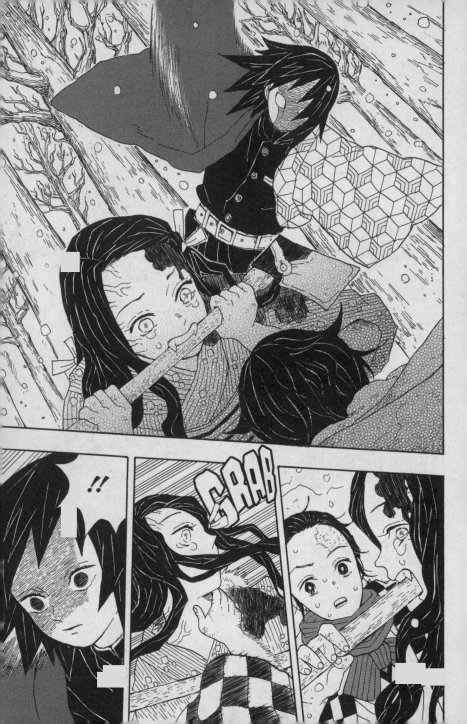

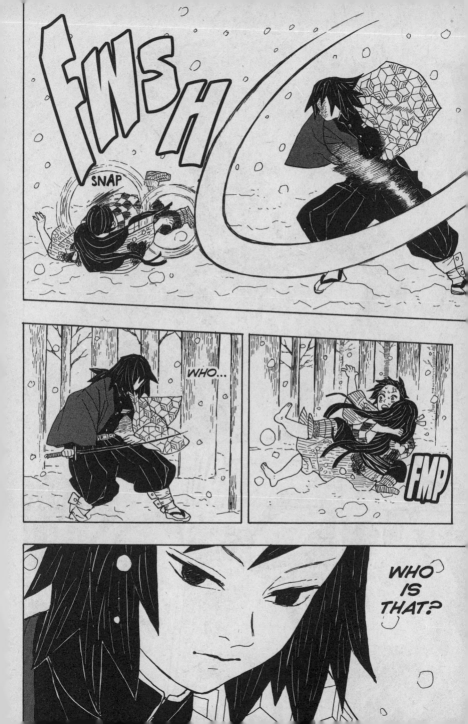

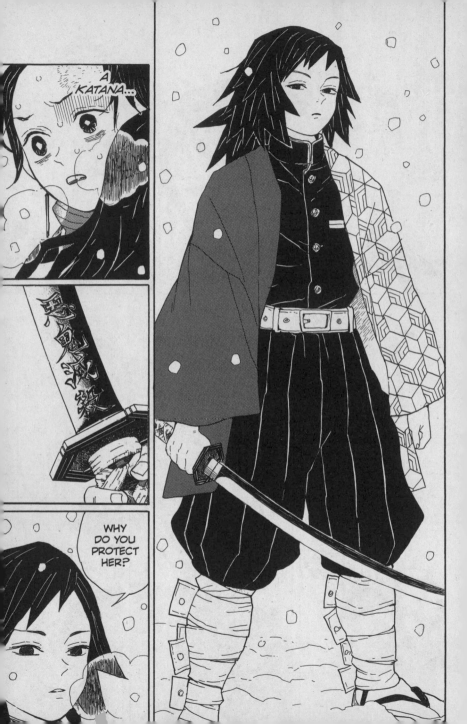

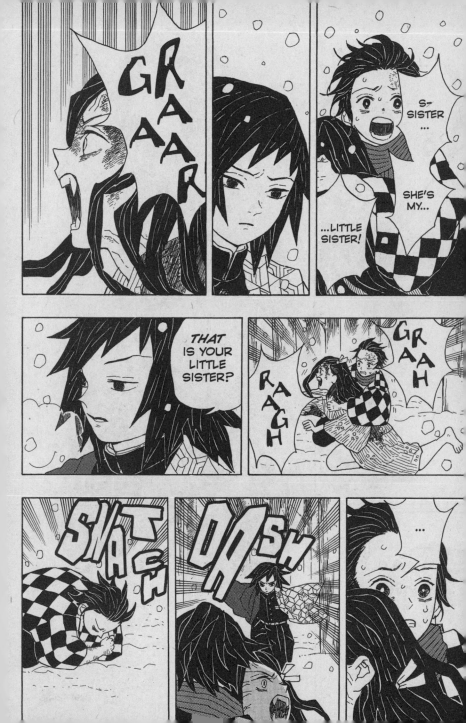

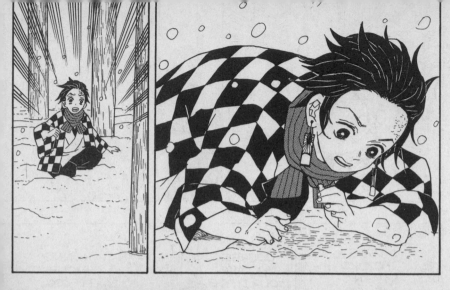

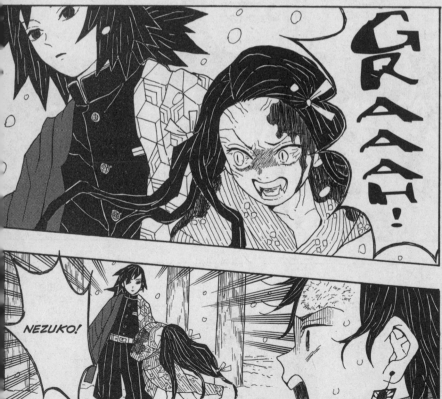

GRAAAH!

NEZUKO!

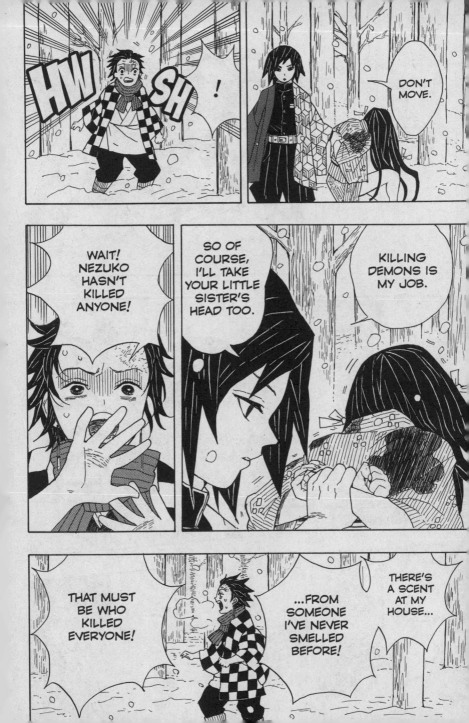

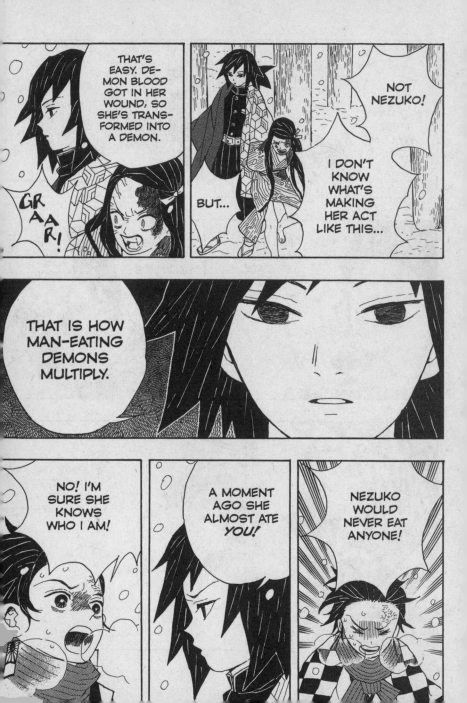

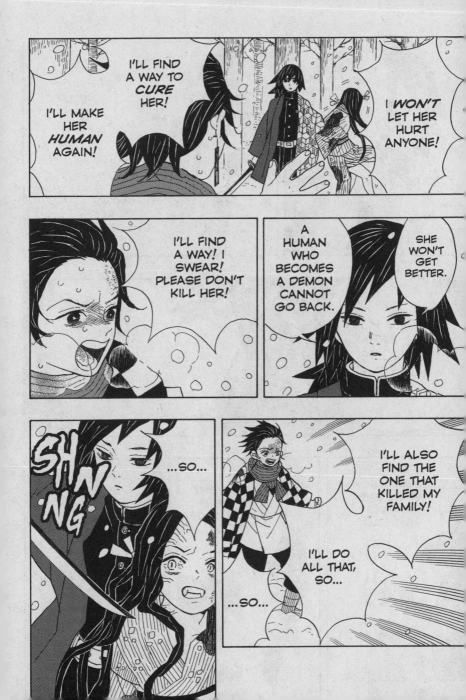

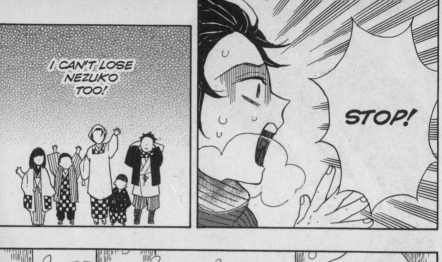

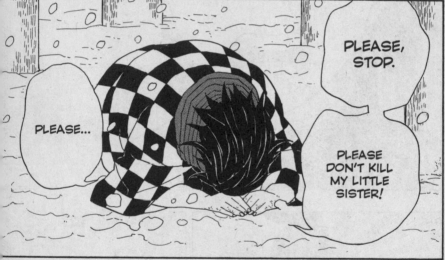

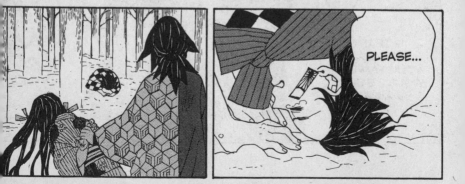

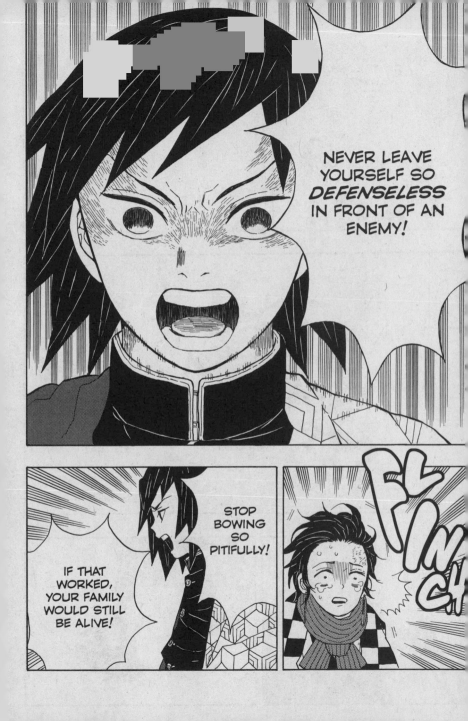

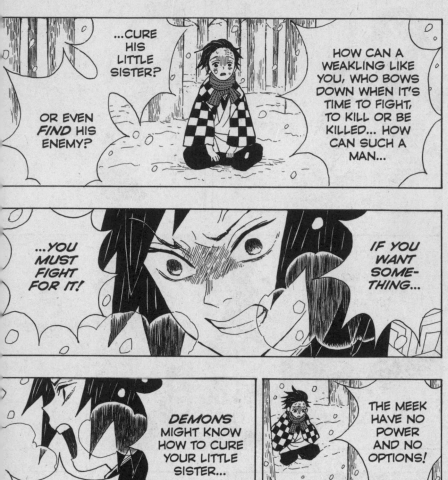

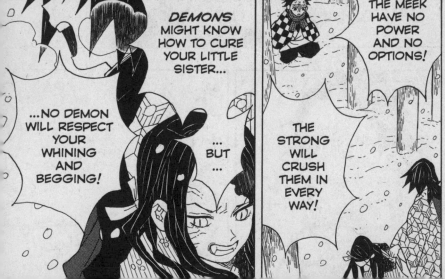

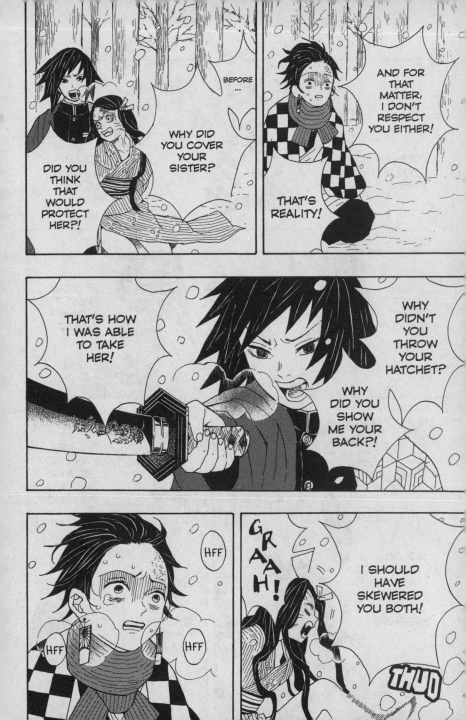

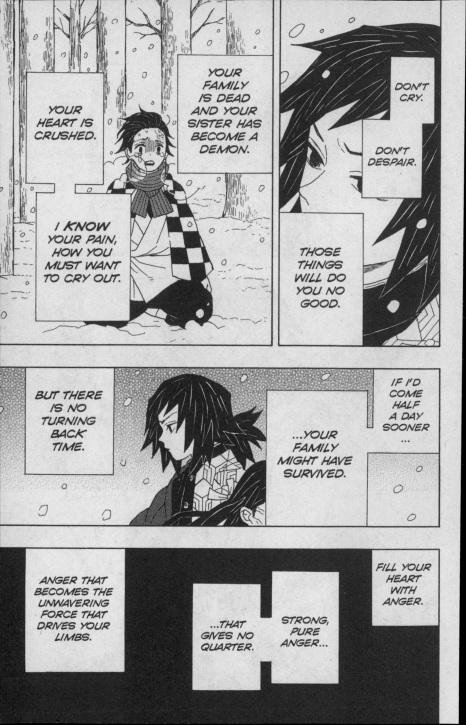

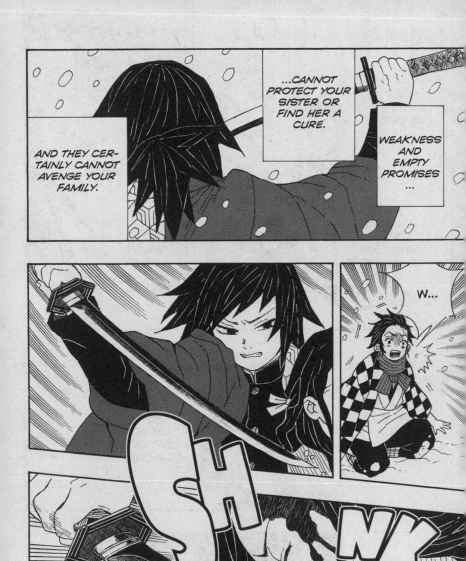

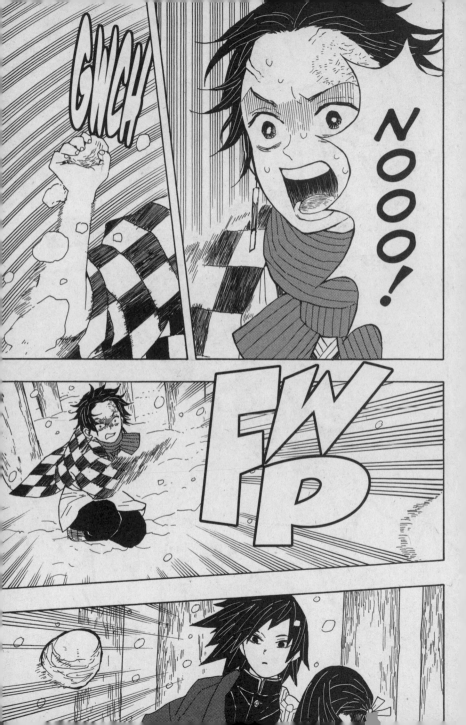

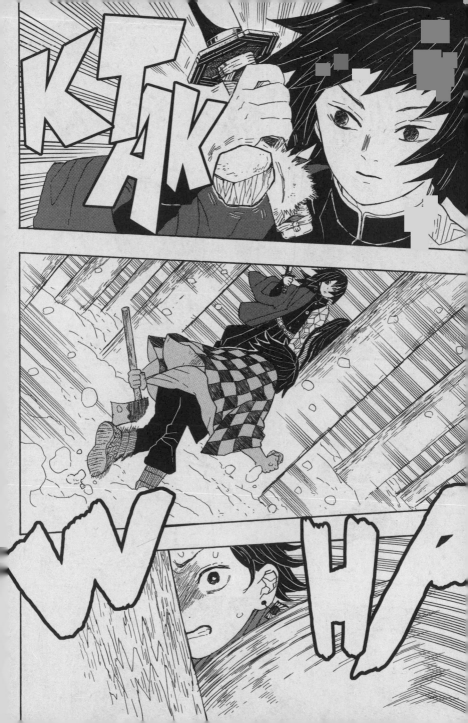

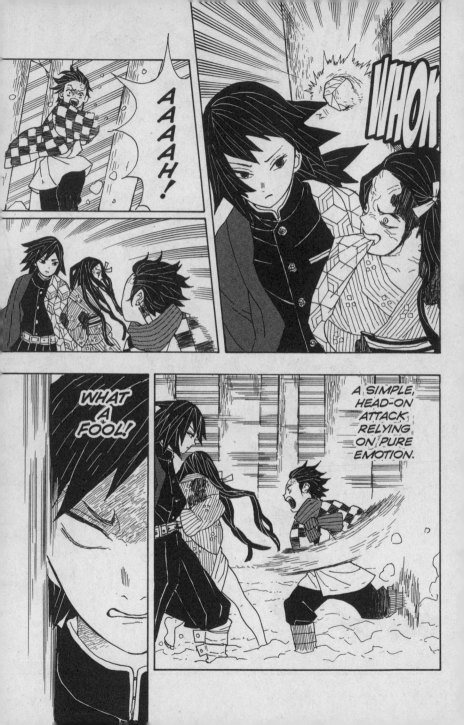

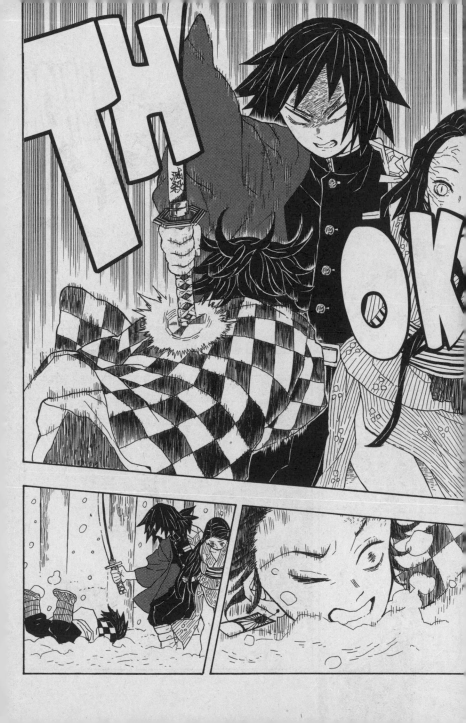

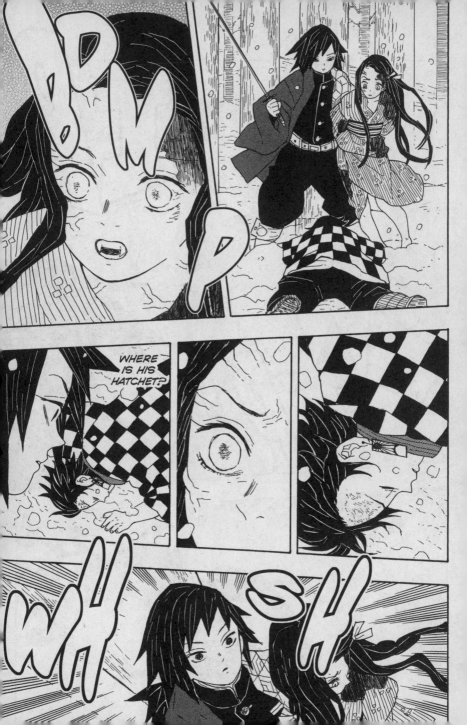

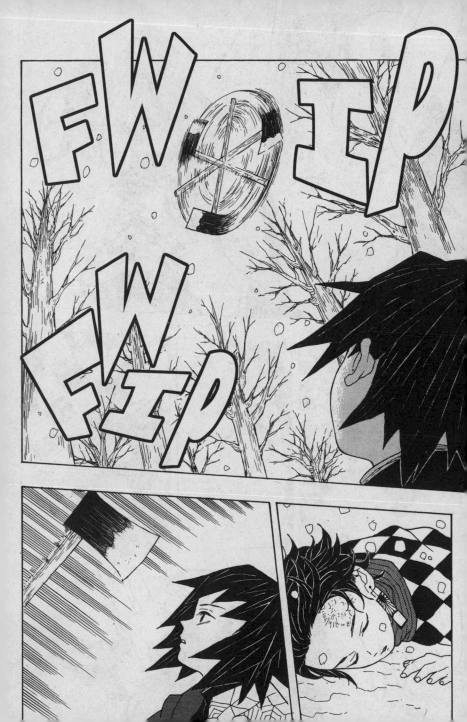

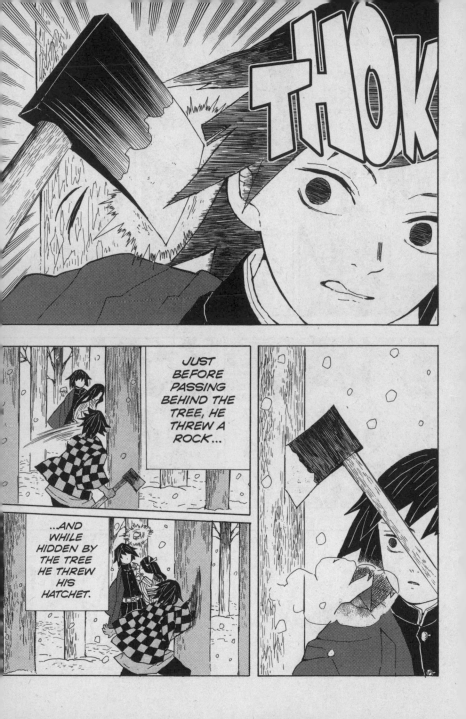

HE HID HIS HAND SO I WOULDN'T SEE HE WAS UNARMED.
HE KNEW HE COULDN'T WIN AGAINST ME, SO HIS PLAN...
...WAS TO STRIKE ME DOWN AFTER I KILLED HIM.
THIS KID...
GRAAR!
WHOK

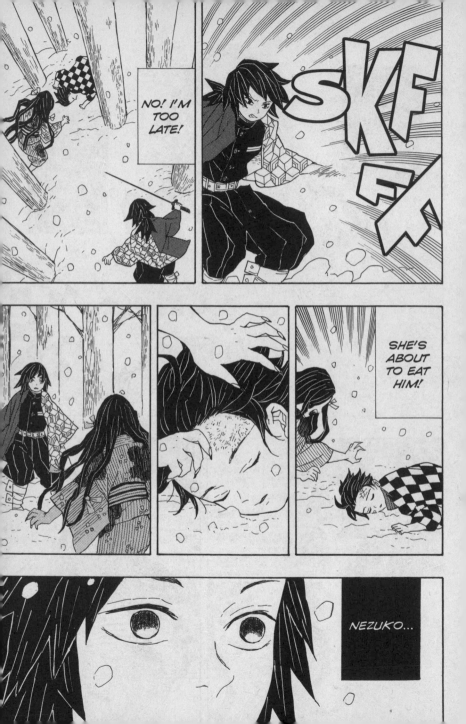

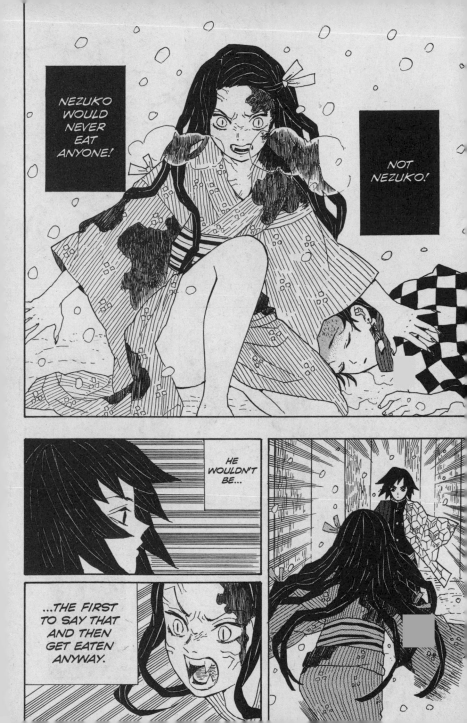

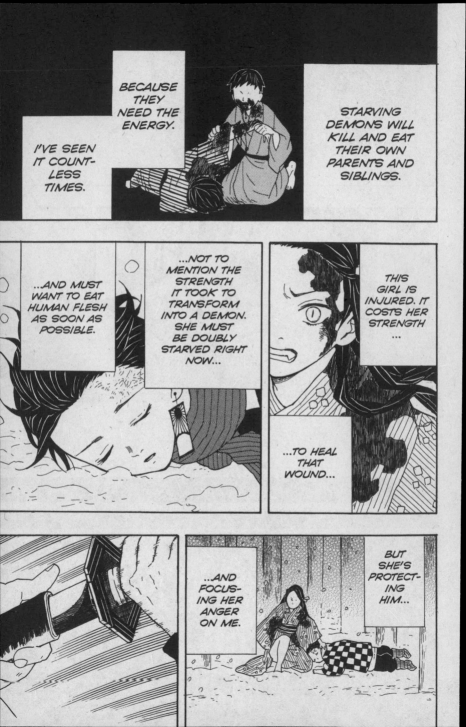

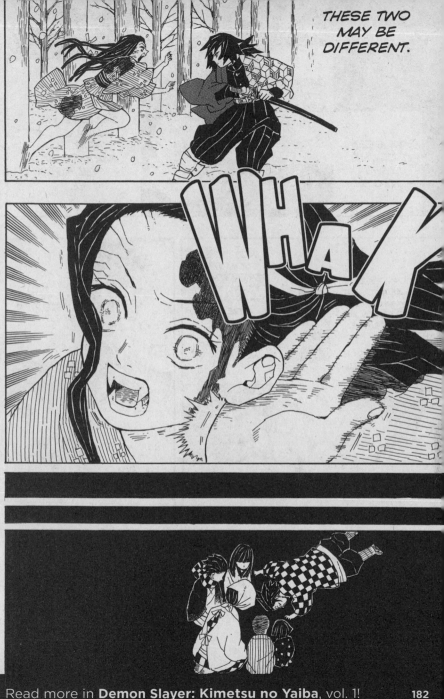

Sleepy Princess in the Demon Castle

Story and Art by Kagiji Kumanomata

Kidnapped by the Demon King and imprisoned in his castle, Princess Syalis is...bored. She decides to while away the hours by sleeping, but getting a good night's rest turns out to be a lot of work! She begins by fashioning a DIY pillow out of the fur of her Teddy Demon guards and an "air mattress" from the magical Shield of the Wielder of the Wind. The princess's hapless demonic guards soon discover that their captive expects to be treated like, well, a princess. Things go from to bad to worse—for her captors— when some of Princess Syalis's schemes end in her untimely—if temporary—demise and she chooses the Forbidden Grimoire for her bedtime reading...

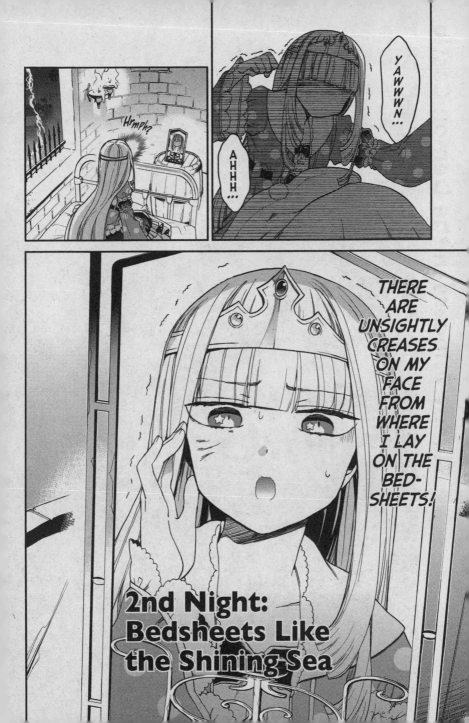

2nd Night: Bedsheets Like the Shining Sea

AND ON TOP OF THAT, I TOSS AND TURN IN MY SLEEP!

Fatal misalignment with the pillow

AGH! I LET MY GUARD DOWN BECAUSE I MADE MY DREAM PILLOW YESTERDAY!

I HAD NO IDEA THE QUALITY OF THE BEDSHEETS IN THE DEMON CASTLE WAS BAD TOO!

BECAUSE IT'S UNCOMFORTABLE WHEN MY BANGS FLOP AROUND...

WHY DID I SLEEP WITH MY CROWN ON?!

SO MY CROWN LEFT A DENT IN MY FOREHEAD TOO...

I NEED A TOOL TO HELP ME WITH DELICATE CRAFTWORK...

BUT WHAT'S THE POINT IF IT DOESN'T LOOK STYLISH AND CUTE...?

Oh!

WHY DON'T I MAKE A HAIR BAND WITH THE LEFTOVER FABRIC FROM MY PILLOWCASE?!

PRINCESS, I'VE BROUGHT YOUR MEAL!

!

Chak

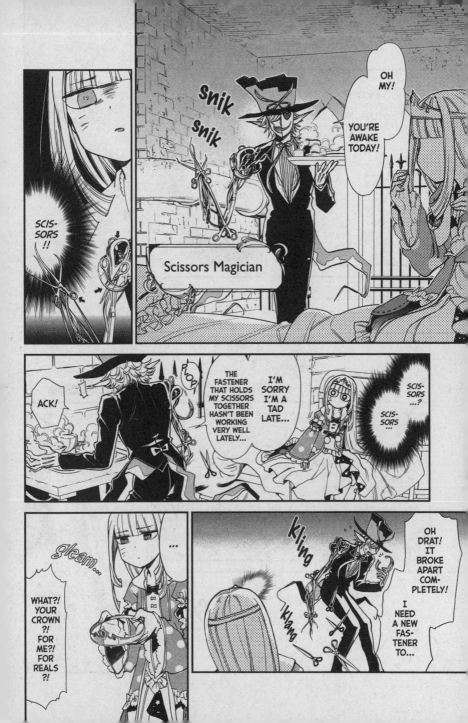

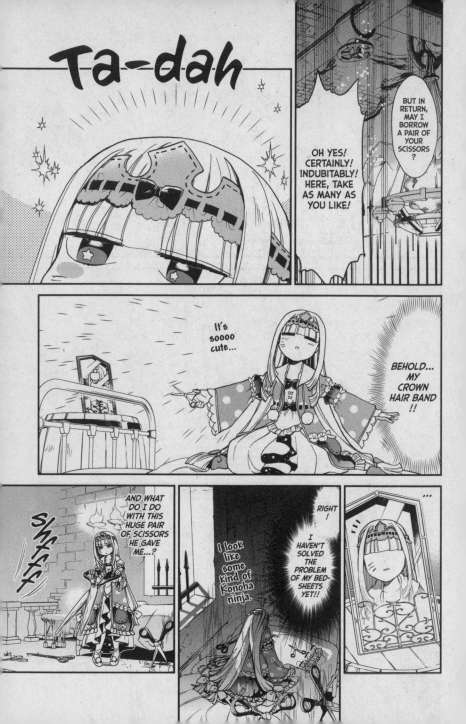

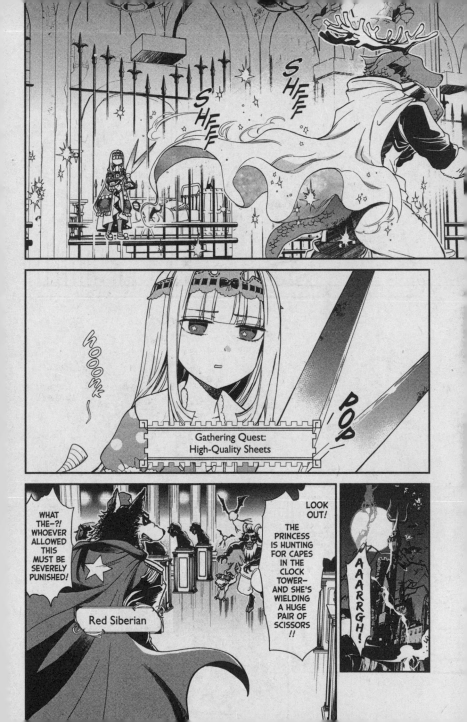

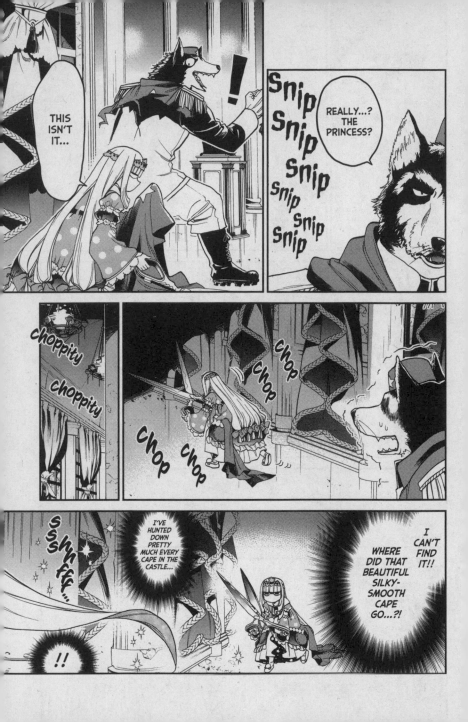

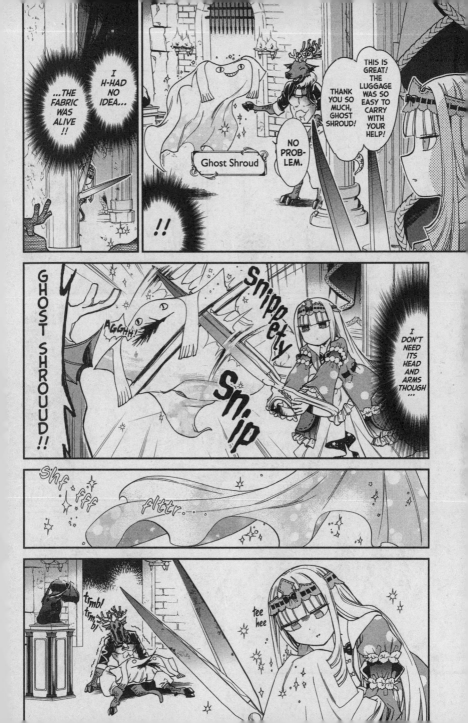

Cool!

Quest Complete

A:ieeee!!

RANK

C

CRITICAL HITS: S
TIME: B
STEALTH: E

...A QUALITY BED-SHEET!!

fWaPPa

I'VE ACQUIRED...

THE FIRST THING I NEED TO DO IS...

ESPECIALLY ONE THAT'S TAKEN SO MUCH EFFORT TO ACQUIRE.

THERE'S A PROCEDURE FOR BREAKING IN A BRAND-NEW BEDSHEET.

tmp tmp tmp

BUT I CAN'T JUST LIE DOWN AND SLEEP ON IT.

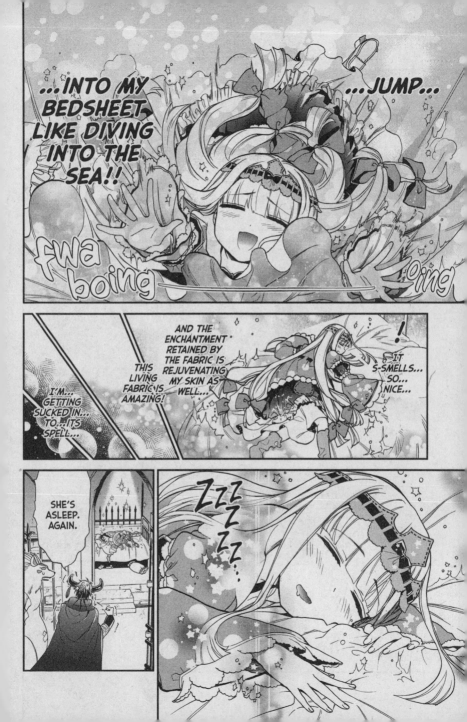

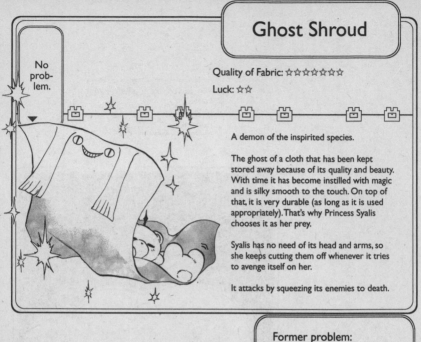

Ghost Shroud

No prob-lem.

Quality of Fabric: ☆☆☆☆☆☆☆

Luck: ☆☆

A demon of the inspirited species.

The ghost of a cloth that has been kept stored away because of its quality and beauty. With time it has become instilled with magic and is silky smooth to the touch. On top of that, it is very durable (as long as it is used appropriately). That's why Princess Syalis chooses it as her prey.

Syalis has no need of its head and arms, so she keeps cutting them off whenever it tries to avenge itself on her.

It attacks by squeezing its enemies to death.

Former problem:
"Lack of presence."

Current problem:
"The princess."

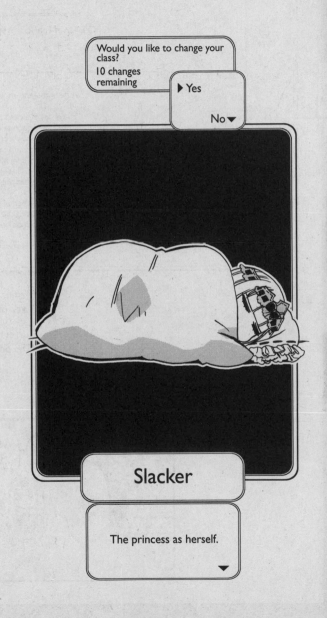

3rd Night: Sweet Sleep Like the Dead

Once upon a time when swords and spells ruled the world...

...and people were threatened by dangerous monsters...

A NEW TYPE OF MONSTER...?

YES.

I ENCOUNTERED THEM NUMEROUS TIMES IN THE NEIGHBORING DESERT.

HMM... THAT MUST BE HARD ON A HERO LIKE YOU.

NO... MY SUFFERING IS INSIGNIFICANT...

tak

tak

...COMPARED TO THE ANGUISH OF PRINCESS SYALIS, HELD CAPTIVE IN THE DEMON CASTLE!

Demon Castle

I'VE HAD IT UP TO HERE!

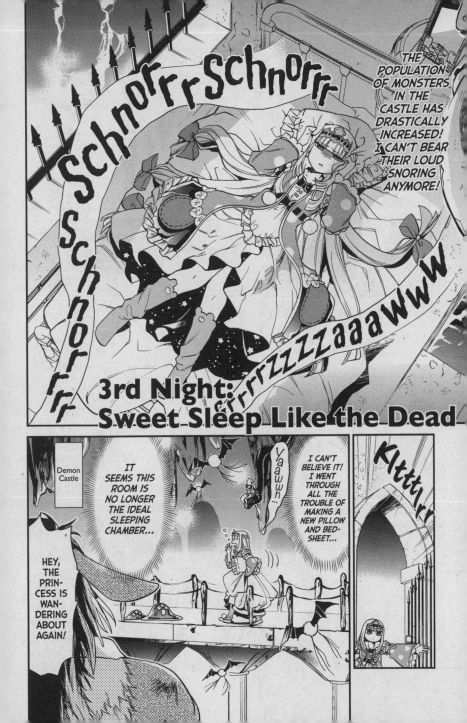

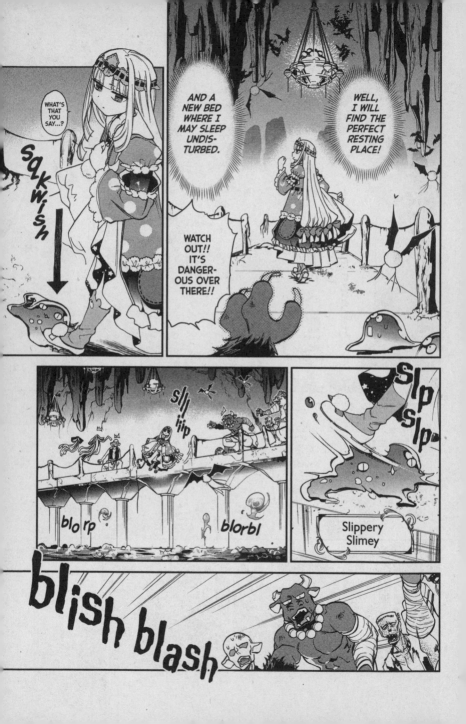

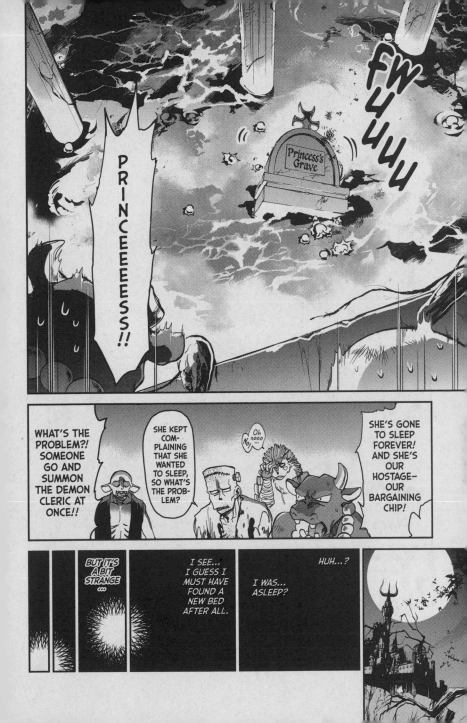

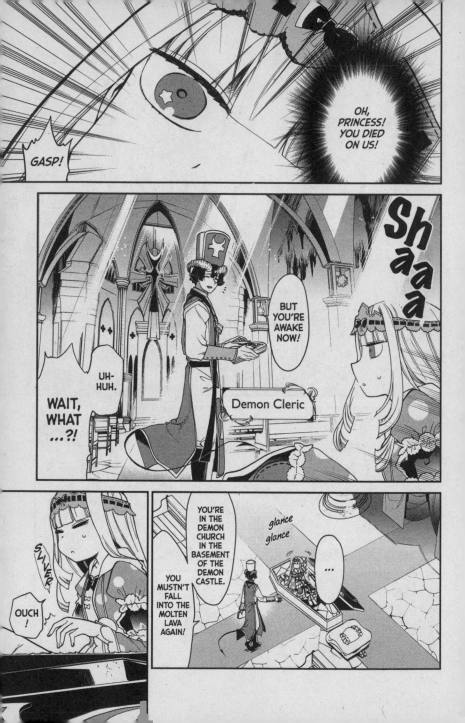

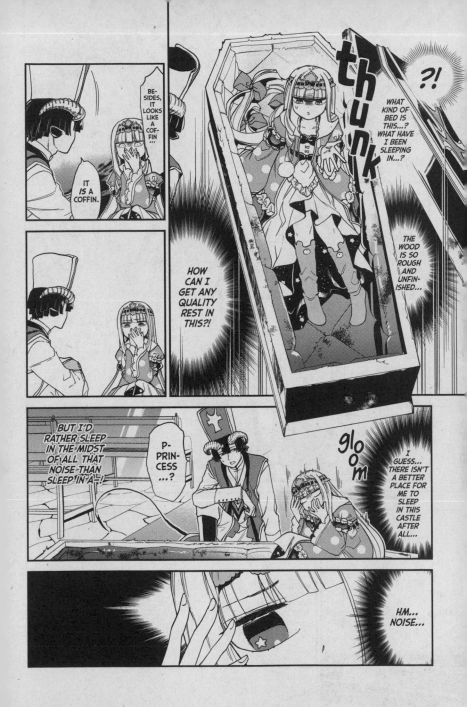

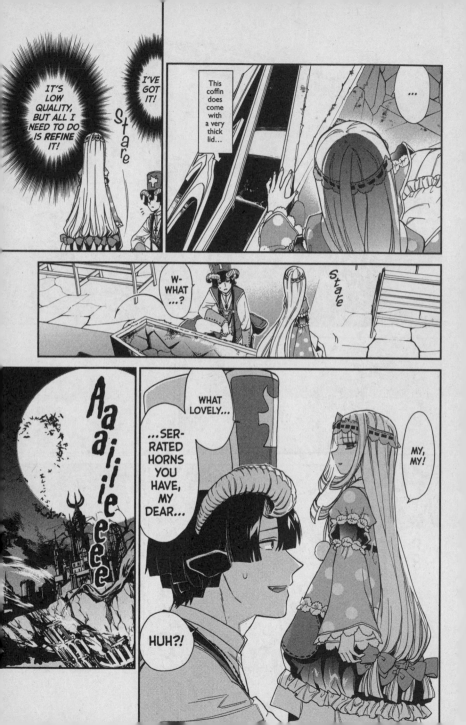

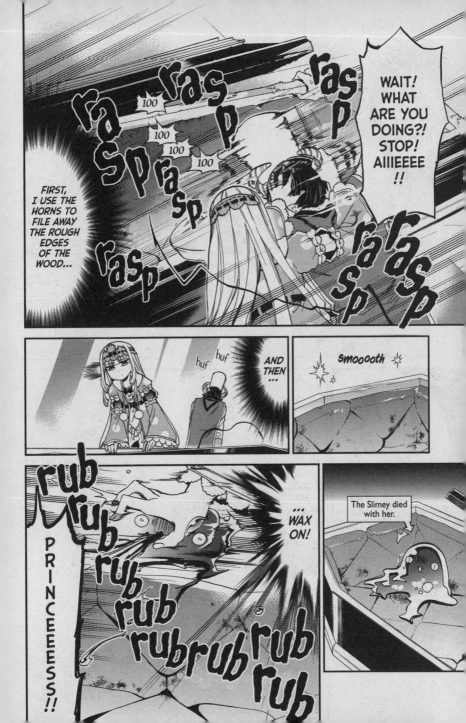

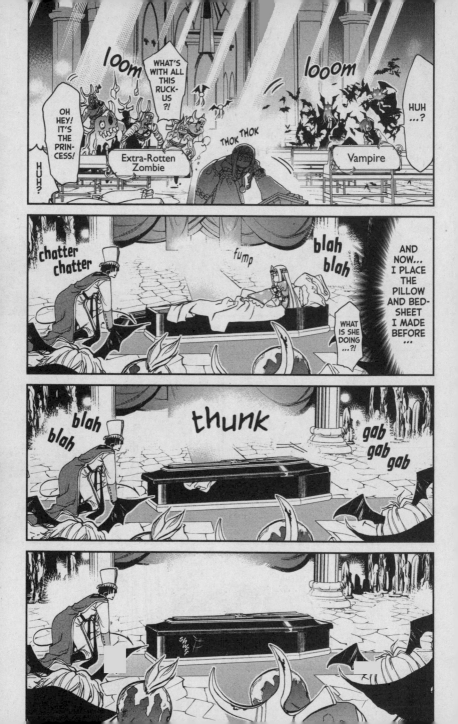

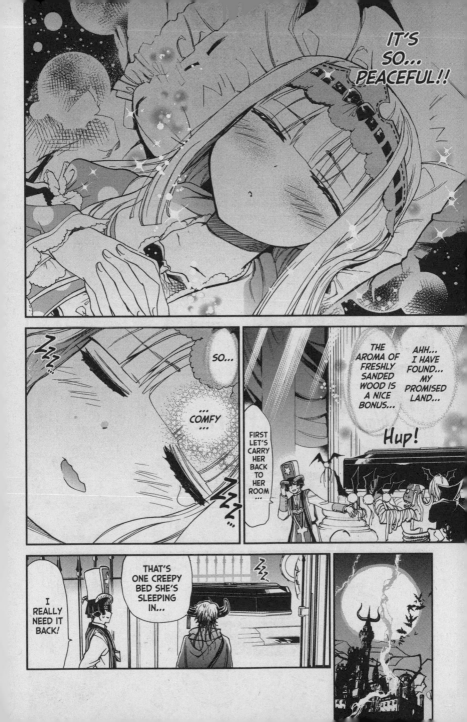

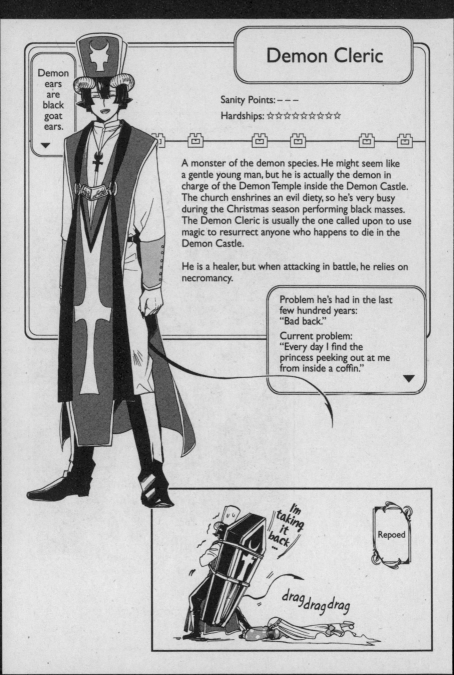

Demon Cleric

Sanity Points: – – –
Hardships: ☆☆☆☆☆☆☆☆

Demon ears are black goat ears. ▼

A monster of the demon species. He might seem like a gentle young man, but he is actually the demon in charge of the Demon Temple inside the Demon Castle. The church enshrines an evil diety, so he's very busy during the Christmas season performing black masses. The Demon Cleric is usually the one called upon to use magic to resurrect anyone who happens to die in the Demon Castle.

He is a healer, but when attacking in battle, he relies on necromancy.

Problem he's had in the last few hundred years:
"Bad back."

Current problem:
"Every day I find the princess peeking out at me from inside a coffin."

▼

I'm taking it back...

drag drag drag

Repoed

Would you like to change
your class?

9 changes remaining

▶ Yes

No ▼

Pugilist

A spotted pug?

▼

In a time long ago when people and demons coexisted in our world...

HEH HEH HEH HEH HEH... YOU SEEM TO BE HAVING A SPOT OF TROUBLE, MY DEAR HERO...

...the hero and his companions entered the Demon King's dungeon...

...to save the kidnapped princess in the Demon Castle.

THAT'S THE VOICE OF THE DEMON KING!!

4th Night: Longing to Sleep on the Shield of the Win

I, DAWNER THE HERO, SHALL SAVE YOU, SYALIS THE PRINCESS, FROM THE CRAMPED CELL YOU'VE BEEN CONFINED TO!!

HAVE YOU FOUND THE SHIELD OF THE WIND YET...?

POOF

TH-THE SHIELD OF THE WIND?!

Fsssshhhhhhh

Demon Castle

D-DAMN IT...!

YOU'LL NEVER BE ABLE TO GET INTO MY FORTRESS WITHOUT IT!

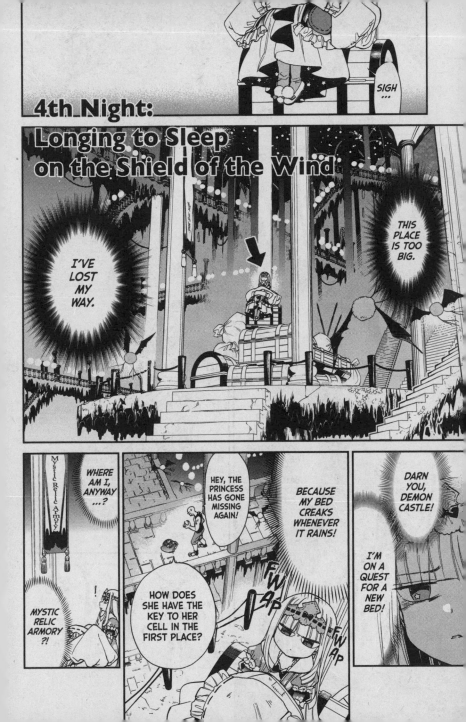

WOOSH

WSh

WHAT KIND OF SHIELD IS THIS...?

THE DEMON KING HAS BAD TASTE IN MYSTIC ARMAMENTS...

Wind gusts out of the shield! ▼

...A LEGENDARY BED (?) OR SOMETHING OF THAT SORT IN HERE...

MAYBE I CAN FIND...

bonk

OUCH!

!!

I'M GOING TO TRIII-IIP...?

trip

?!

Wicked Diamond

shuv

I HAVE NO USE FOR THIS.

FLOAT

?!

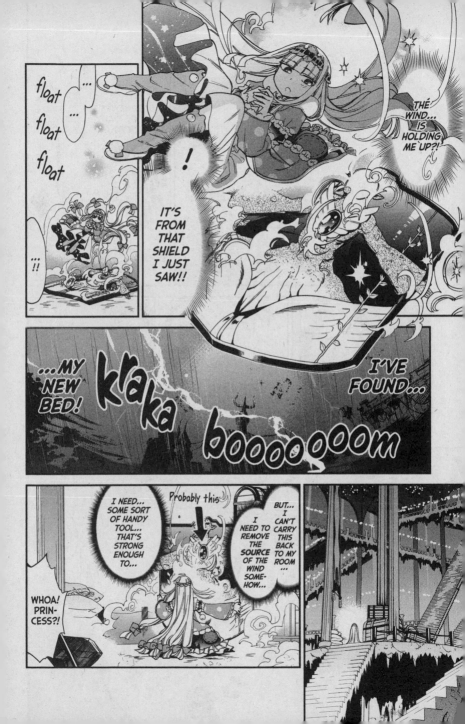

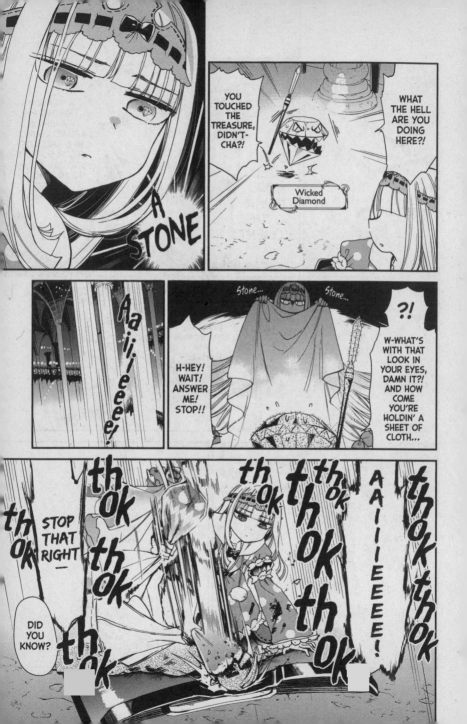

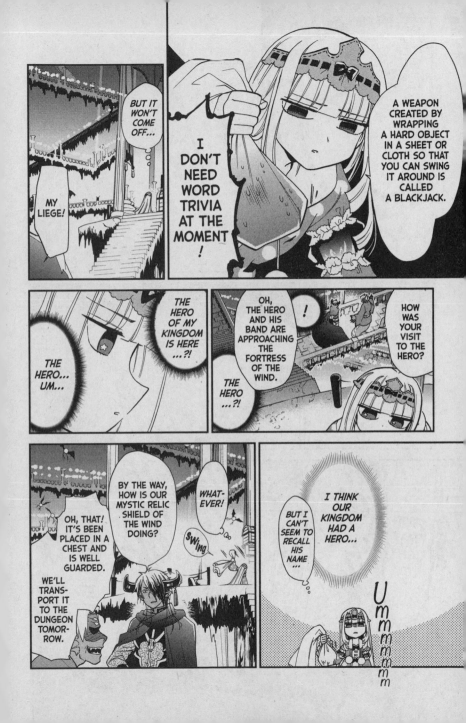

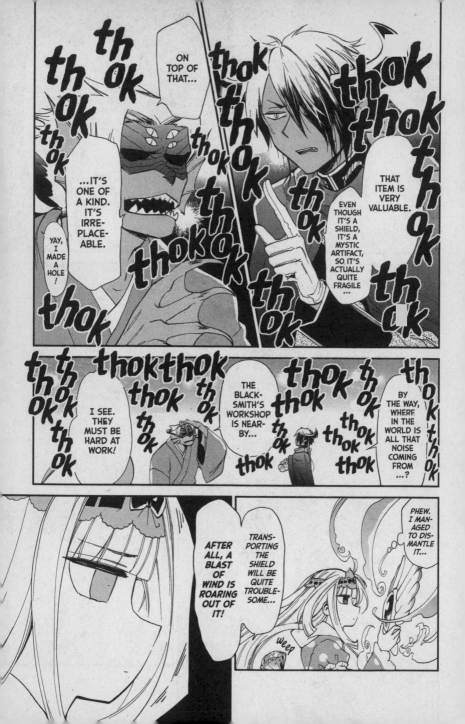

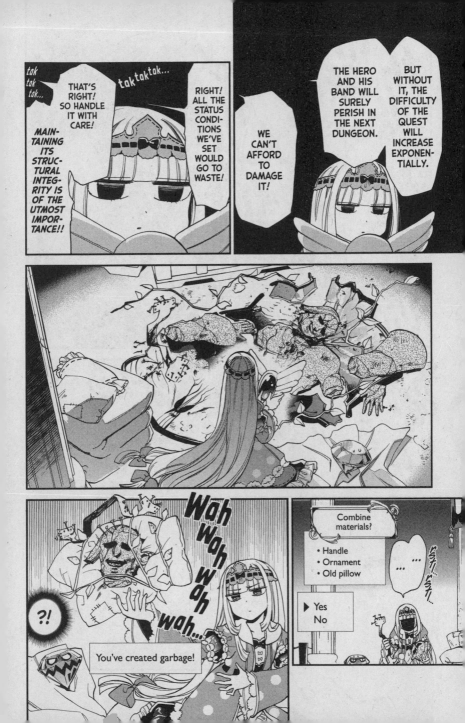

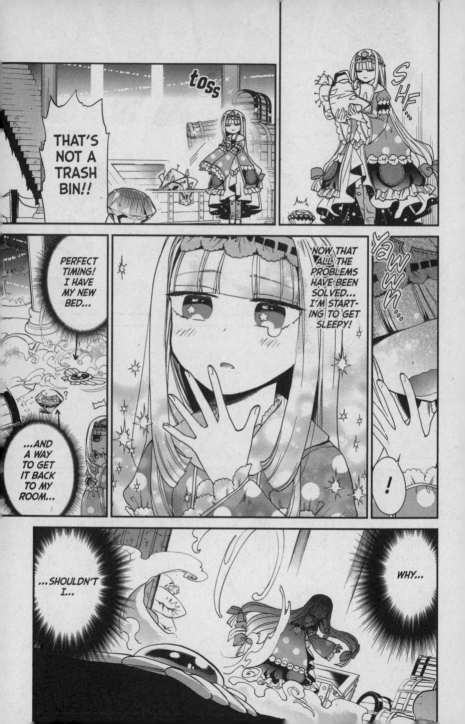

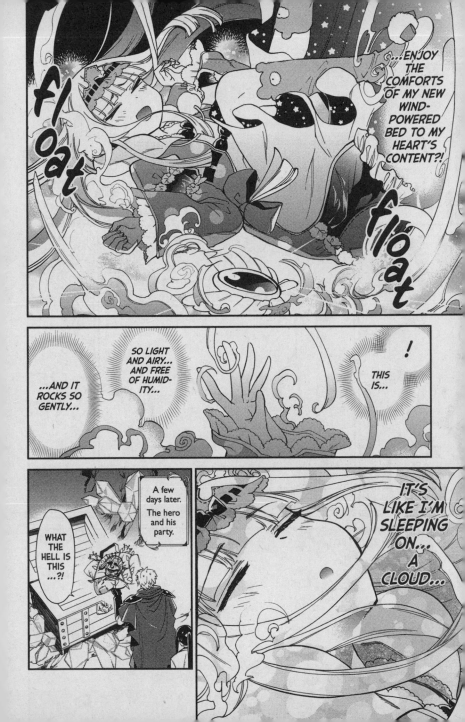

> He's supposed to be powerful.

▼

Dawner the Hero

Courage: ☆☆☆☆☆☆☆
Presence: ☆

The hero who has appeared to save the kidnapped princess. Human. As a hero, he lives to rescue princesses.

The Unified Human Nation of Goodereste has great faith in Dawner, and he has been credited with many noble deeds, so Princess Syalis has definitely met him before. But for some reason, he leaves no memorable impression on her.

Favorite food: "Goodereste-style meat loaf."

▼

HUH...? WHAT IS THAT?!

What is this?

sneaky sneak

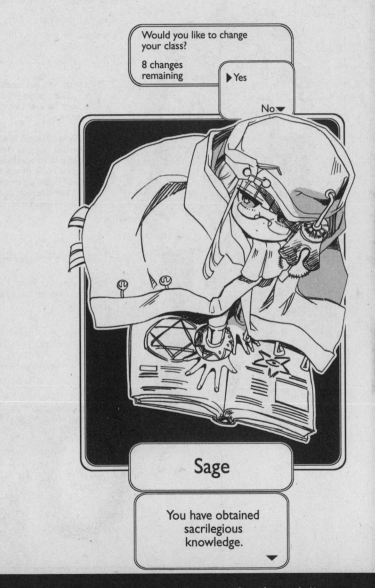

Takane & Hana

Story and Art by Yuki Shiwasu

After her older sister refuses to go to an arranged marriage meeting with Takane Saibara, the heir to a vast business fortune, high schooler Hana Nonomura agrees to be her stand-in to save face for the family. But when these two utter opposites pair up, get ready for some sparks to fly!

●●●●● WING 4G   12:25   71% ▬

< Message   **Dad**   Contacts

Can you do me a massive favor!!!! 🙏🙏

Are you serious?

Today 12:25

💣💣💣 It's urgent! 💣💣💣 🐵
Young Mr. Saibara 📞 me!!!
He's coming to pick you up at
7pm at the 🏠, so make sure
you're home by then. 🎀🎀
BTW, sounds like he hasn't
figured out who you really are.
(´∀`)ノ 🎊🎊

WHAT
CAN THAT
MEAN?!

So he's
ignoring that
whole thing
with my
wig?

?!

B A G G Y

THAT'S
A LOW-
SLUNG
CAR!

Whoa!

Sister's
clothes

OVERSIZED
CLOTHING
IS WHAT'S
POPULAR
THESE DAYS?

...

LEAVE
ME
ALONE.

WHAT
DO YOU
WANT,
TAKANE?

HE'D BETTER NOT
SAY SOMETHING
STUPID LIKE
"YOUR BEHAVIOR
YESTERDAY GOT
ME INTERESTED
IN YOU."

HMPH

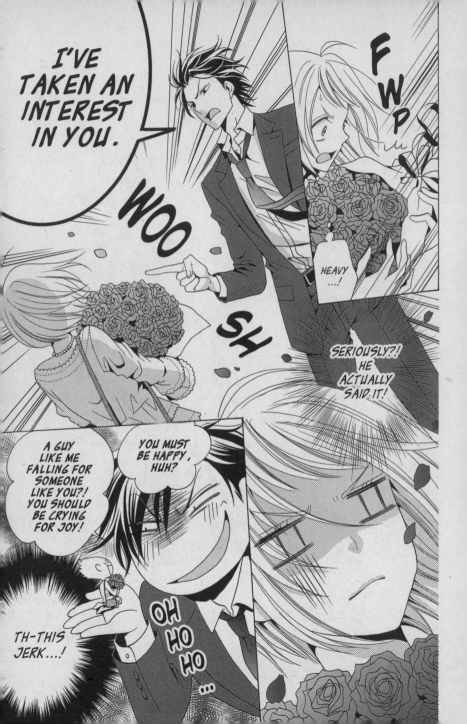

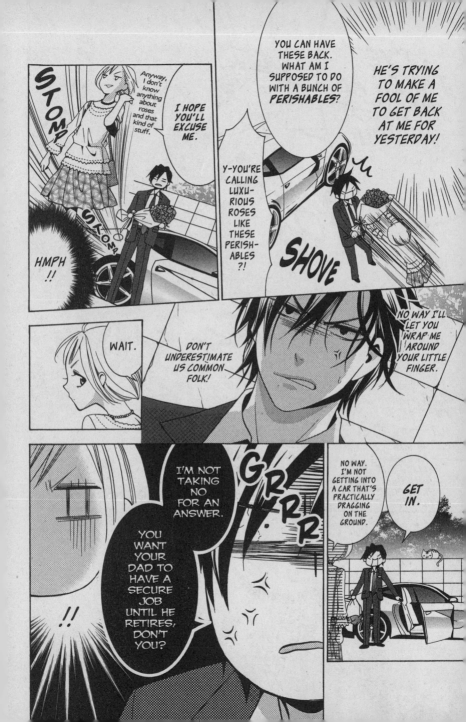

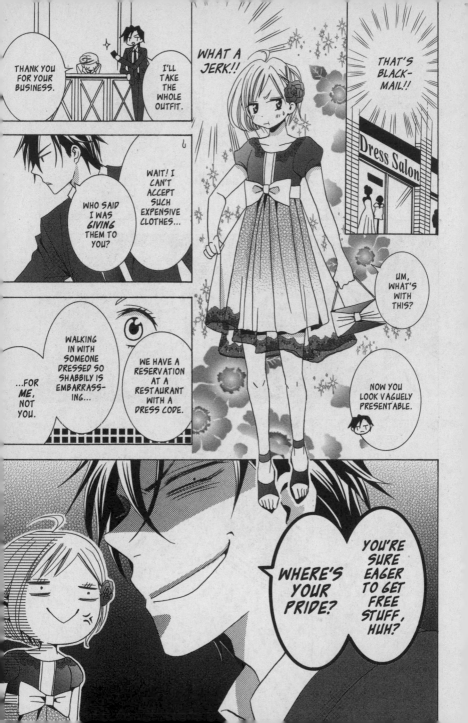

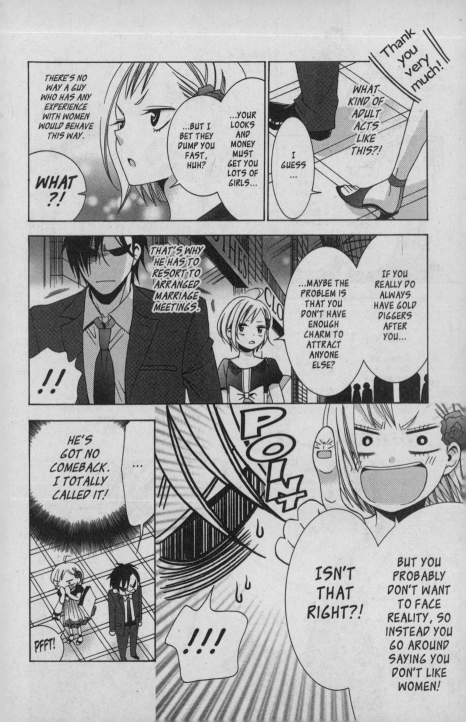

PLUS, I FOUND OUT THAT MEETING WAS ALL MY GRAND-FATHER'S IDEA.

Or some-thing.

...MAY HAVE...

...SAID SOME THINGS YESTER-DAY THAT WERE OUT OF LINE.

Maybe.

I...

HAH!

WHIRL

...RRY...

WHAT?

MUMBLE

I'M SORRY ...!

DID YOU COME HERE TODAY TO APOLOGIZE?

I CAN'T DO IT. ONE MORE APOLOGY AND I'LL PUKE.

THAT'S NOT A NORMAL PHYSICAL REACTION.

HUF HUF

SORRY, BUT I DIDN'T CATCH THAT.

ALL RIGHT, LET'S SEE IF HE'LL SAY IT AGAIN.

WAIT...

Um...

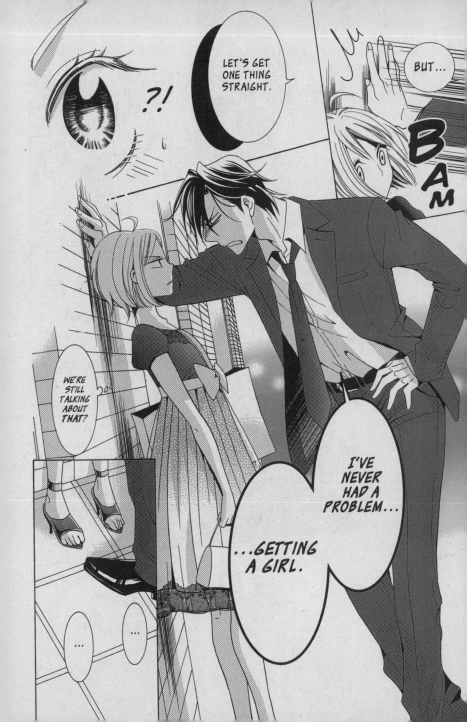

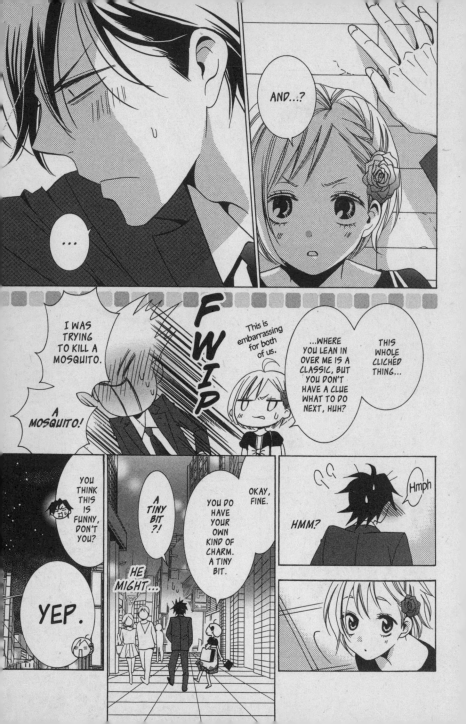

...NOT BE A BAD GUY AFTER ALL.

Ha Ha! Ha ha ha!

You don't know etiquette at all! How embarrassing!

BUT HE STILL PISSES ME OFF.

Takane, the parking lot's over there.

IT'S HILARIOUS!

Shall I buy you some chocolate truffles?

I'm perfectly capable of buying my own.

Pfft! (LOL)

Total culture shock...

Wait, truffles are mushrooms? That's so weird.

BUT YOU SAID—

NAH.

THANK YOU FOR DINNER.

KEEP THEM.

I DON'T HAVE ANYWHERE TO STORE THEM.

I'LL SEND THE CLOTHES BACK ONCE I'VE HAD THEM CLEANED.

NO WAY!

BOW

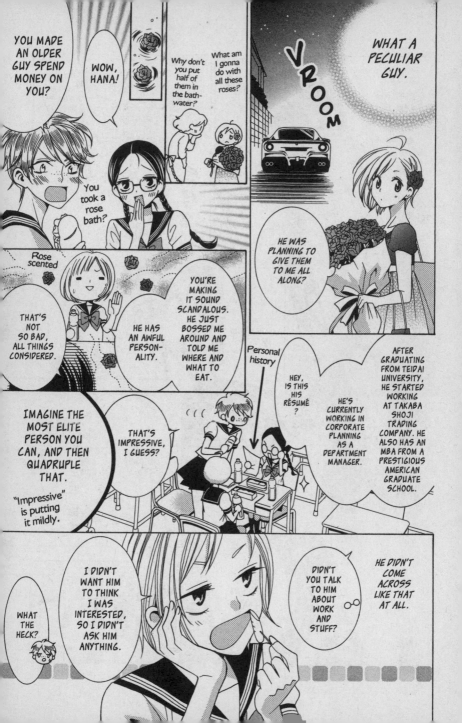

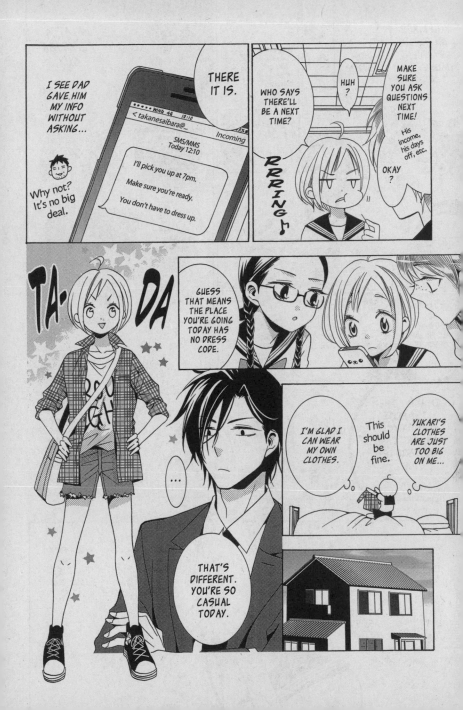

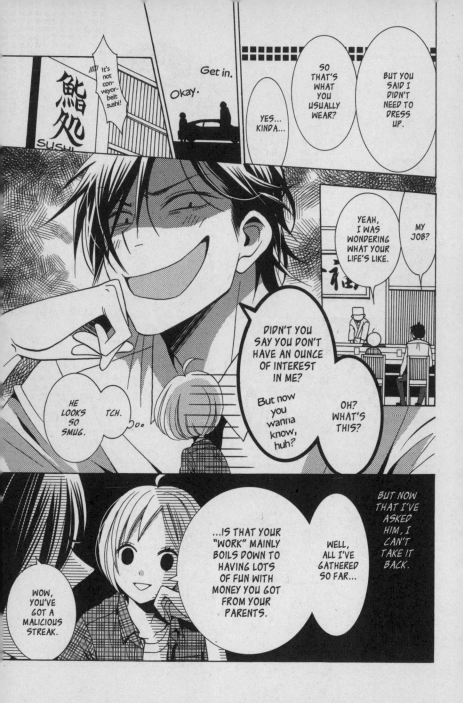

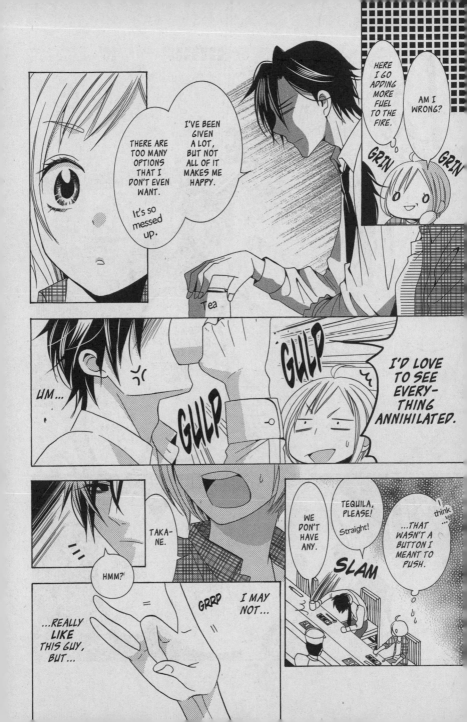

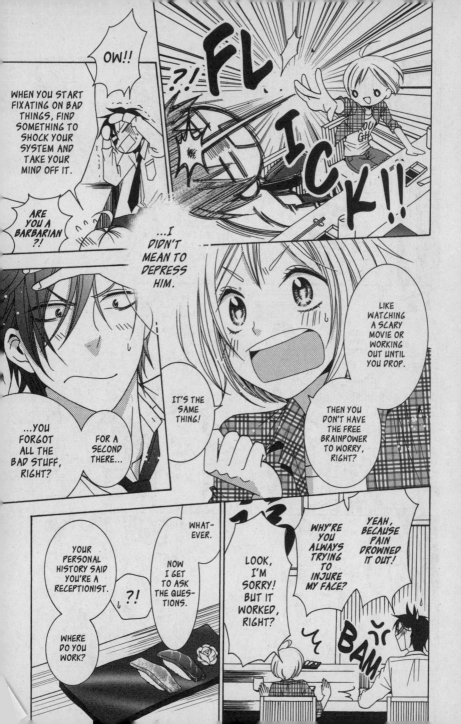

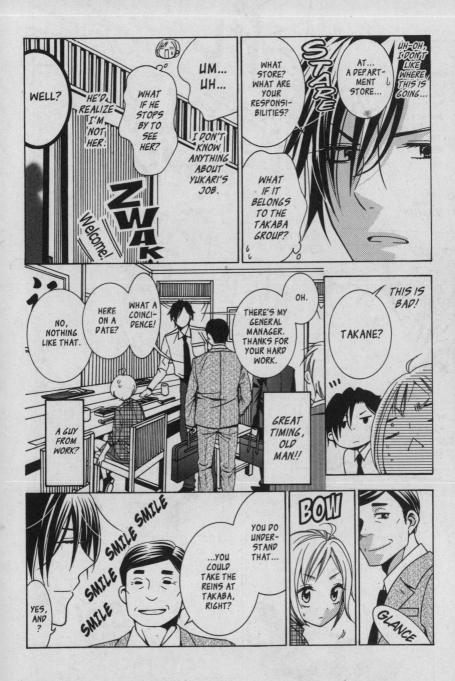

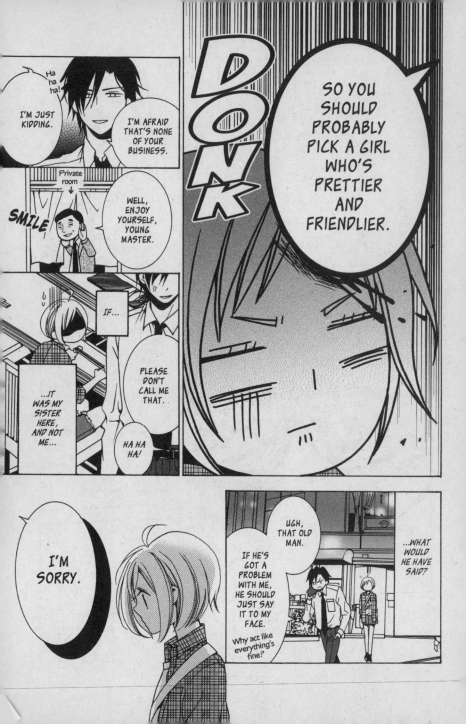

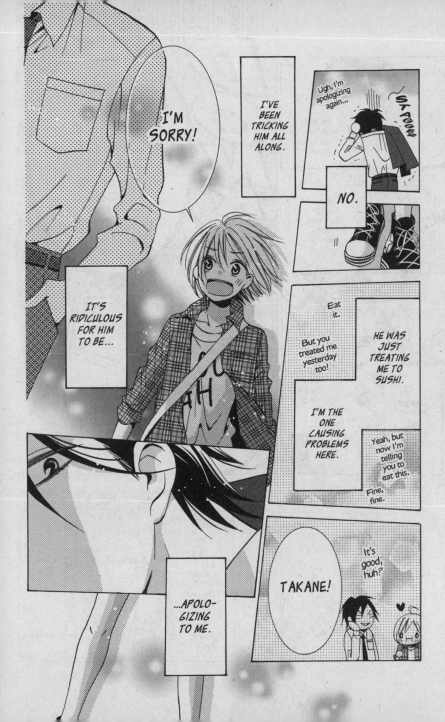

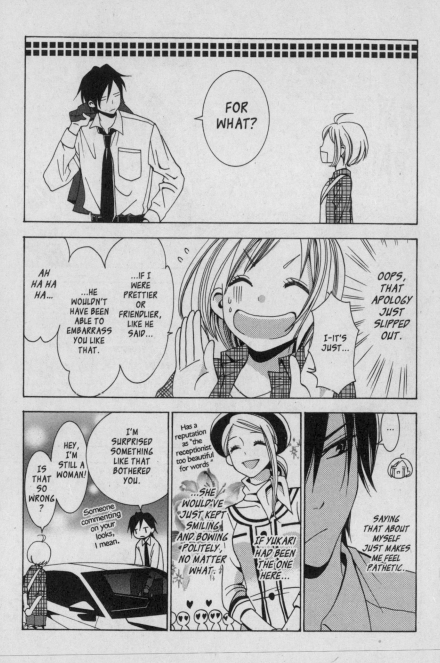

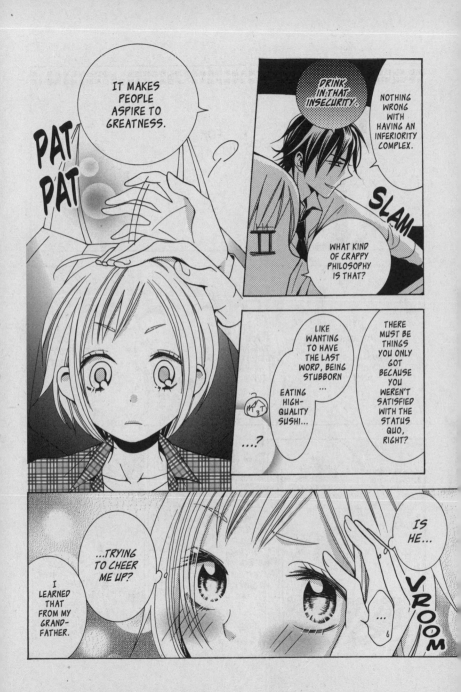

SEAT BELT.

MAYBE HE'S...

Oh.

RIGHT.

...MORE GROWN-UP THAN I THOUGHT.

NOPE, HE'S AS IMMATURE AS BEFORE.

FORGET I SAID ANYTHING.

YOU SURE ARE INTERESTED IN ME TODAY.

WHAT ABOUT YOU? DO YOU HAVE SOME SORT OF...

...COMPLEX TOO?

Monthly allowance: 3,000 yen (about $30)

HMM...

HEY! THAT COST ME 400 YEN, YOU KNOW!

TRUFFLES THAT NORMAL PEOPLE EAT MAY BE INEXPENSIVE, BUT THEY'RE STILL DELICIOUS!

IT'S NOT MUCH, BUT IT'S TO THANK YOU FOR YESTERDAY AND TODAY.

HERE.

Chocolate

GANACHE TRUFFLES

INTENSE

ANAC

POP

Oh.

SEE YA.

HUH...

I still bet that happens to him a lot.

You need to actually *say* these things. That's why you always get dumped.

SO EATING IT IN FRONT OF ME WAS HIS WAY OF SAYING "YOU'RE WELCOME"?

HE ATE IT!

MNCH MNCH

MNCH MNCH MNCH

HEH

WHAT A WEIRDO.

MNCH MNCH CH MNCH

WHY IS THIS SO GOOD?!

MN

GANACHE TRUFFLES

"WILL HE BE BACK TOMORROW?"

Too bad he's lousy at expressing his emotions.

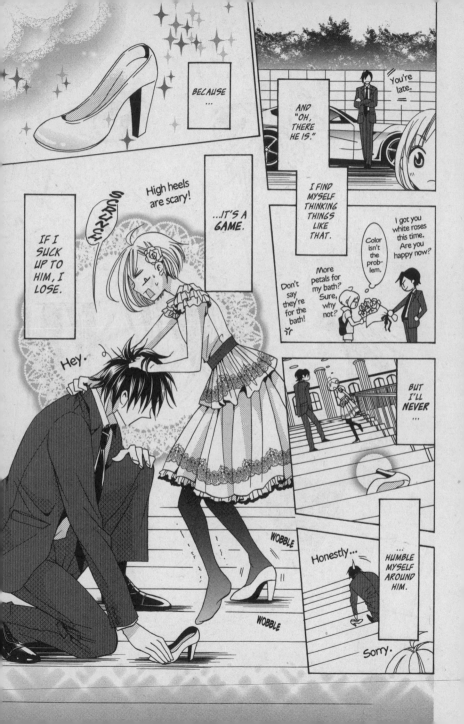

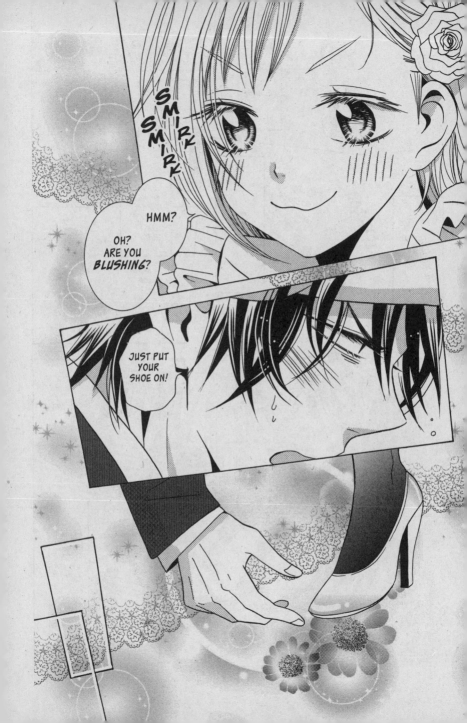

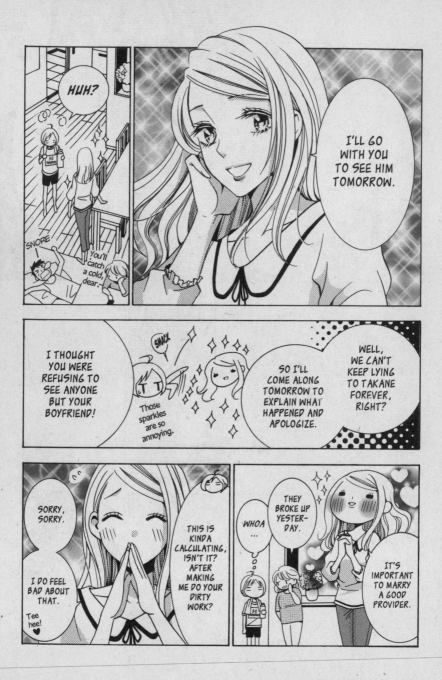

BUT COME ON, HANA.

HOW LONG DO YOU THINK YOU CAN PRETEND TO BE ME?

Think about the consequences.

...ISN'T IT BETTER TO TELL HIM DIRECTLY?

HE'LL FIGURE IT OUT EVENTUALLY, SO...

Delicious Milk

3-2 Tsunomiya

WHAT STYLE DO YOU THINK HE LIKES?

HOW'S THIS?

What shall I wear?

THAT MIGHT BE TRUE, BUT...

THAT'S WHAT I WORE WHEN I MET HIM...

Those sleeves were full-length on me.

OKAY, IT'S SETTLED!

YEAH, THAT'S GOOD ENOUGH.

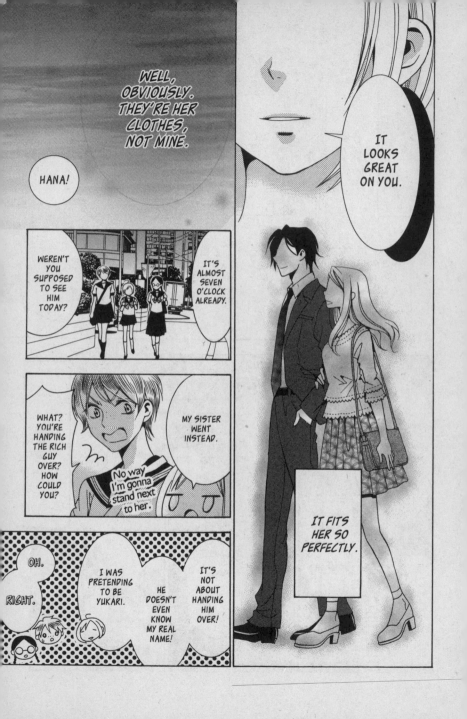

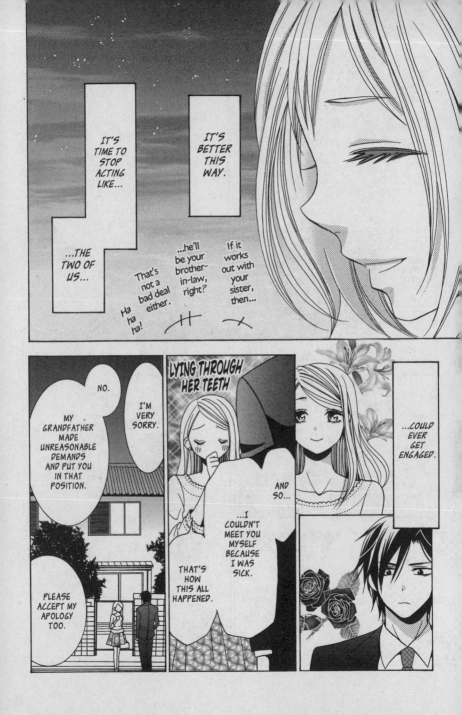

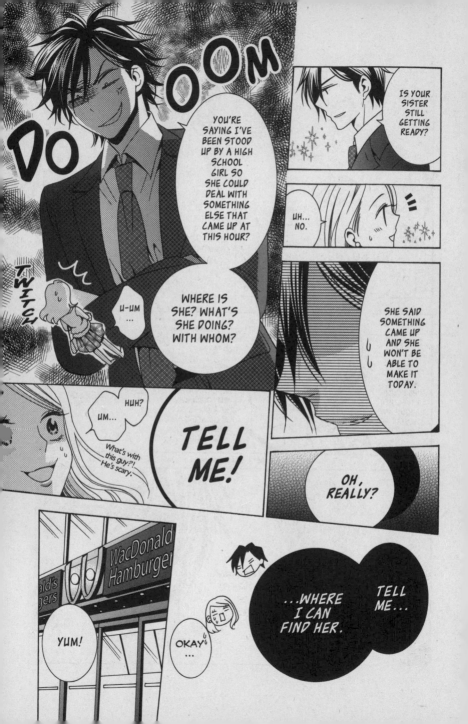

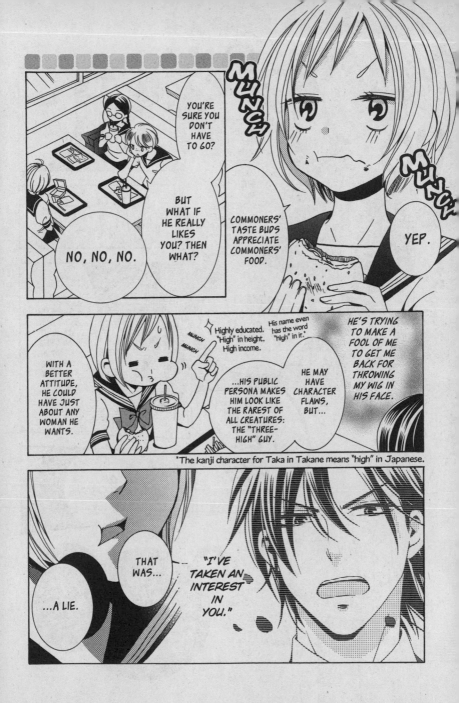

...LYING TO BE WITH ME.

...HOW I WAS LYING TO HIM TO BE WITH HIM.

JUST LIKE...

TAKANE WAS...

HANA...

HERE YOU GO.

Handkerchief

PLIP

HUH?

THAT'S ALL THERE IS TO IT.

IT WAS THAT SIMPLE, AND NOW IT'S OVER. THAT'S ALL.

OH!

I TEARED UP OVER HOW TASTY THIS IS...

WHAT THE HECK?

HEY!

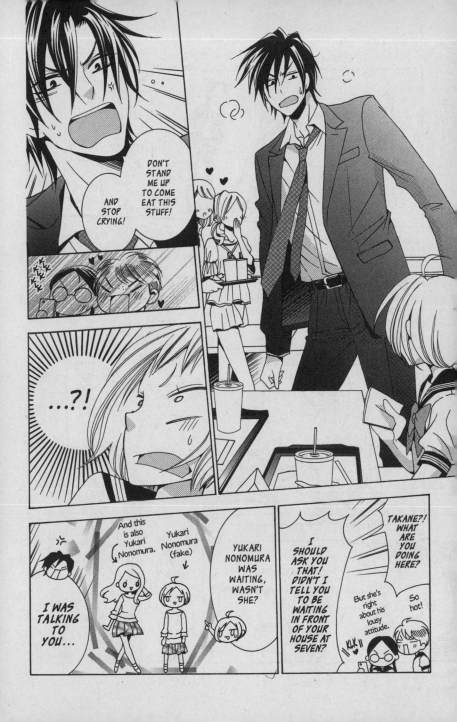

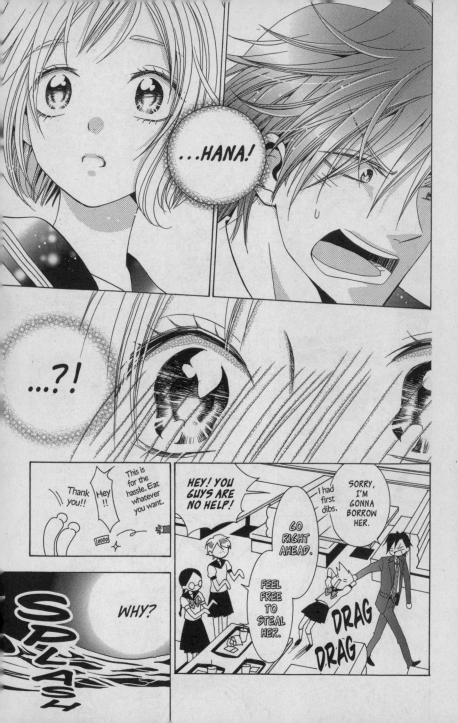

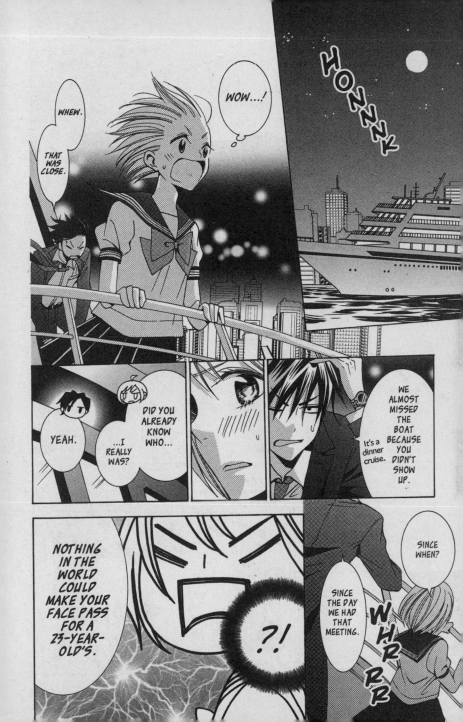

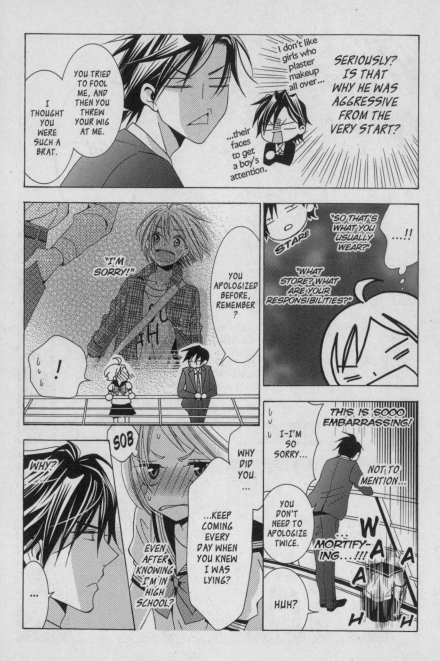

I DON'T KNOW.
HUH?!
WHY THE HECK AM I SPENDING LOADS OF MONEY SO I CAN MAKE A FOOL OF A BRAT WHO PISSES ME OFF?
HOW SHOULD I KNOW?!
AND I WAS RIGHT! YOU WERE TRYING TO MAKE ME LOOK STUPID!
YOU MUST'VE SPENT HUNDREDS OF DOLLARS IN THE LAST FEW DAYS, RIGHT?
MORE THAN THAT.
AND WHAT DO YOU MEAN, YOU DON'T KNOW?!
YOU CALL YOUR-SELF AN ADULT?!
I-I DON'T USUALLY DO STUPID THINGS LIKE THIS!
THEN WHY—?!

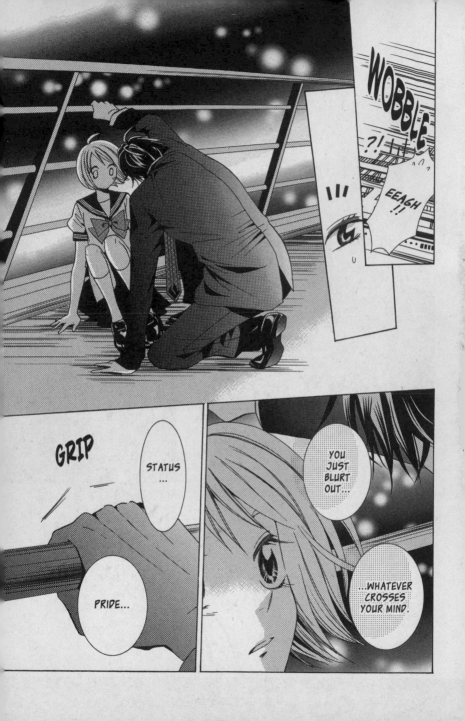

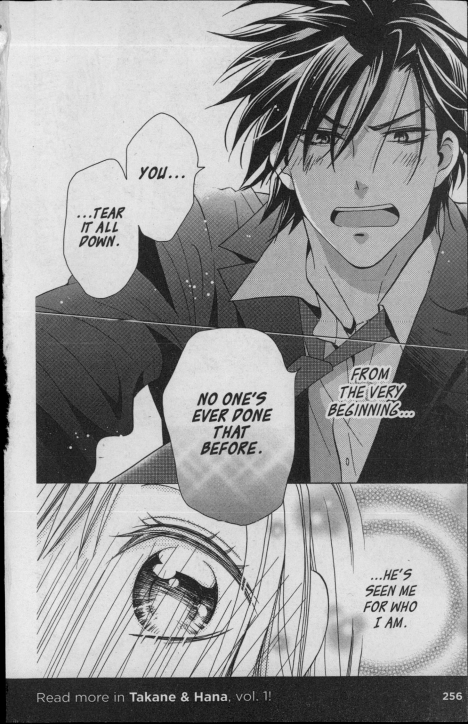

TABLE OF CONTENTS

VIZ
MANGA
SAMPLER
2018

Introduction

VIZ Media has an excellent lineup of great new manga series for 2018. This year our offerings include a manga adaptation of the hit animated series *RWBY*, hilarious shojo rom-coms, engrossing fantasy series and a spin-off of the hit *Shonen Jump* series *My Hero Academia*. We hope you enjoy this sampler of some of our new favorites.